REGGE POLES AND S-MATRIX THEORY

Frontiers in Physics

A Lecture Note and Reprint Series

DAVID PINES, ***Editor***

P. W. Anderson **CONCEPTS IN SOLIDS:** *Lectures on the Theory of Solids*

N. Bloembergen **NUCLEAR MAGNETIC RELAXATION:** *A Reprint Volume*

Geoffrey F. Chew **S-MATRIX THEORY OF STRONG INTERACTIONS:** *A Lecture Note and Reprint Volume*

R. P. Feynman **QUANTUM ELECTRODYNAMICS:** *A Lecture Note and Reprint Volume*

R. P. Feynman **THE THEORY OF FUNDAMENTAL PROCESSES:** *A Lecture Note Volume*

Hans Frauenfelder **THE MÖSSBAUER EFFECT:** *A Collection of Reprints with an Introduction*

Robert Hofstadter **NUCLEAR AND NUCLEON STRUCTURE:** *A Reprint Volume*

Leo P. Kadanoff and Gordon Baym
QUANTUM STATISTICAL MECHANICS: *A Lecture Note Volume*

A. M. Lane **RECENT DEVELOPMENTS IN NUCLEAR THEORY:** *A Lecture Note and Reprint Volume*

R. Omnès and M. Froissart
MANDELSTAM THEORY AND REGGE POLES: *An Introduction for Experimentalists*

George E. Pake **PARAMAGNETIC RESONANCE:** *An Introductory Monograph*

David Pines **THE MANY-BODY PROBLEM:** *A Lecture Note and Reprint Volume*

E. J. Squires **COMPLEX ANGULAR MOMENTA AND PARTICLE PHYSICS:** *A Lecture Note and Reprint Volume*

L. Van Hove, N. M. Hugenholtz, and L. P. Howland
PROBLEMS IN THE QUANTUM THEORY OF MANY-PARTICLE SYSTEMS: *A Reprint Volume*

P. Nozières **THEORY OF INTERACTING FERMI SYSTEMS:** *An Introductory Monograph*

S. C. Frautschi **REGGE POLES & S-MATRIX THEORY:** *A Lecture Note Volume*

TATA INSTITUTE OF FUNDAMENTAL RESEARCH

REGGE POLES
AND
S-MATRIX THEORY

STEVEN C. FRAUTSCHI
California Institute of Technology

W. A. BENJAMIN, INC. *1963*
New York *Amsterdam*

REGGE POLES AND S-MATRIX THEORY

Library of Congress Catalog Card Number 63-22796
Manufactured in the United States of America

Final camera copy for this volume was prepared under the direction of Dr. Frautschi and was received on October 5, 1963; the volume was published on December 16, 1963.

The publisher is pleased to acknowledge the assistance of William Prokos, who designed the cover.

W. A. BENJAMIN, INC.
New York City, New York

Preface

Most of the lectures in this book were first given as theoretical seminars at Cornell University during 1961-1962, and were then augmented and brought into final form for the Summer School in Theoretical Physics held at Bangalore in June 1962. Some more recent developments are discussed in two Addenda.

Regge poles enter in the latter half of the lectures after the analogies and conceptual difficulties that led to their introduction into relativistic physics have been explained. It is anticipated that some readers will be interested exclusively in the simpler aspects of Regge poles, however. Readers in this category are advised to concentrate upon the following sections of the book: the treatment of ordinary quantum mechanics in Chapters X and XI [through Equation (11-11)], and the connection of Regge poles with relativistic scattering in Chapters XIII (first two paragraphs), XIV, XV, and XVI.

The material in Chapter II is on a similar level and is intended to give some physical feeling for S-matrix theory in its simpler manifestations. The chapters on the Mandelstam representation are more weighty and will be of interest primarily to the theoretical student who wishes to work in this field.

STEVEN C. FRAUTSCHI

Pasadena, California
September 1963

Contents

I. INTRODUCTION

A considerable number of strongly interacting particles is now known. For experimental reasons, the particles stable under strong interactions tended to be discovered first, and were followed by the pion-nucleon resonances and, recently, a large number of other resonances. The situation now bears some resemblance to nuclear physics: for each set of quantum numbers there appears to be a "ground level" and various unstable states with higher mass.

Early attempts to cope with these particles theoretically often followed the line of attack that had proved so successful in quantum electrodynamics. A simple Lagrangian was chosen, with renormalized couplings and masses given, and the other physical observables were calculated by a perturbation expansion. But this approach failed to give good predictions because the coupling was strong and the perturbation expansion converged slowly. In fact, when some of the particles are resonances or bound states as suggested by analogy with nuclear physics, the perturbation expansion will not converge at all. Therefore, a modified approach is needed. The S-matrix methods described in these lectures represent a modified approach which works even where perturbation expansions fail.

Since the S-matrix represents a meeting ground between theory and experiment, most of the S-matrix techniques we shall describe can be used whether or not one believes in some particular underlying structure, such as Lagrangian field theory. But, in addition to its use as a tool in evaluating the consequences of various theories, the S-matrix appears to provide hints on some fundamental questions:

i) Is there any essential difference between stable and unstable particles, other than the presence of states to decay into? In nuclear physics, the answer is no, whereas in some early treatments of Lagrangian field theory, a distinction appeared to arise because one did not know how to introduce unstable particles into the Lagrangian. In S-matrix theory, the distinction does not appear. (This is also true in recent treatments of field theory.)

ii) Can masses and coupling constants be calculated? If a particle appears only when the forces become strongly attractive, then its mass and couplings are calculable. We call such a particle a <u>bound state</u> if it is stable, a <u>resonance</u> if it is unstable, and <u>composite</u> in either case. It is also possible to introduce particles into the S-matrix, which are present independently of the strength or sign of the forces. The masses and couplings of these particles cannot be calculated -- just as masses and couplings inserted into a Lagrangian are arbitrary -- and we choose to call such particles <u>elementary</u> since we cannot explain them. Both composite and elementary particles may be either stable or unstable. The possibility of finding experimental distinctions between them is of great interest and may be provided by Regge poles as we shall see.

iii) How many arbitrary masses and coupling constants are present in strong interactions? There is no way to deduce this at present. But a study of the S-matrix as a function of energy, momentum transfer, angular momentum, etc., produces a suggestive fact -- the analytic structure of the S-matrix as a function of these variables becomes simpler as the number of independent parameters is reduced. This observation has led to the hypothesis of maximal analyticity -- the analytic structure of the S-matrix is as simple as possible.[1] If this hypothesis is correct, there are no arbitrary constants in strong interaction physics except for c, $\hbar$, and one mass, and all strongly interacting particles are composite.

The hypothesis of maximal analyticity raises many questions. It has no evident connection to previous starting points such as Lagrangian theory; it seems to call for a new axiomatic framework expressed directly in terms of the S-matrix. Stapp[2] has proposed such a framework, and the reader is referred to his lectures[2] for a detailed account. Then there is the practical question of how to make calculations when nothing is "given". For this purpose, "bootstrap calculations" based on self-consistency requirements have been devised.[3] Another question concerns the uniqueness of the solution. The actual strong interactions possess the property of maximal strength,[4,5] in the sense that high-energy total cross sections approach a constant geometrical limit. We shall take this property from experiment; it is not known whether it follows uniquely from maximal analyticity. Likewise, we shall take the usual conservation laws of isotopic spin, strangeness, electric charge, and so forth, from experiment, without knowing whether some of them can ultimately be derived.

Before plunging into details of analytic structure, let us devote a few words to the meaning of singularities. Why must there be poles and cuts in the S-matrix even when "maximal analyticity" is assumed? Above threshold at kinetic energies Re $q^2/2m + i\epsilon$, an outgoing solution of the Schrodinger partial-wave equation acquires a phase $2\delta_\ell$ at large distances. The S-matrix in this case is defined as

$$S(q,\ell) = e^{2i\delta_\ell(q)} \quad . \tag{1-1}$$

The time-reversed solution at Re $q^2/2m - i\epsilon$ has a reversed phase factor $\exp(-2i\delta_\ell)$, resulting in a discontinuity of S. Physically, the discontinuity arises because we are comparing two solutions related by a discontinuous transformation (time reversal).

Below threshold, q^2 becomes negative and q becomes purely imaginary. The asymptotic wave function, which had the form

$$u(q) \sim e^{-iqr} - e^{-i\pi\ell}\, S(q,\ell)\, e^{+iqr} \tag{1-2}$$

above threshold, becomes

$$u(iq_I) \sim e^{q_I r} - e^{-i\pi\ell}\, S(iq_I, \ell)\, e^{-q_I r} \quad . \tag{1-3}$$

Usually, the wave function cannot be normalized. But at a bound state, only the converging exponential is present, and this requires $S = \infty$ (normally provided by a pole) at $q_I > 0$ and $S = 0$ at $q_I < 0$. For a given bound state, both the pole and the zero occur since the Schrödinger equation is invariant under $q \to -q$.

II. EFFECTIVE RANGE THEORY OF S-WAVE SCATTERING, AND THE N/D METHOD

The effective range formula for S-wave scattering contains a good deal of low-energy physics. At the same time it is very simple, and its properties in the complex energy plane can be followed explicitly.[6] To get a physical feeling for the complex energy plane we shall consider the effective range formula in detail, relating the analyticity properties to physical properties at each step.

The S-wave elastic scattering amplitude

$$f_o = \frac{e^{i\delta_o} \sin \delta_o}{q} \tag{2-1}$$

can be rewritten:

$$f_o = \frac{\sin \delta_o}{(\cos \delta_o - i \sin \delta_o) q} = \frac{1}{q \cot \delta_o - i q} \quad . \tag{2-2}$$

The effective range approximation is given by

$$q \cot \delta_o = -\frac{1}{A} + \frac{R}{2} q^2 \quad , \tag{2-3}$$

where A is called the scattering length and R the effective range. So we have

$$f_o = \frac{1}{-\frac{1}{A} + \frac{R}{2} q^2 - i q} \quad . \tag{2-4}$$

This approximation is valid near threshold for short-range potentials.

Since the denominator of (2-4) is quadratic in q, f_o evidently has two poles in q. As a function of q^2, it also has a cut which can be taken along the real axis from $q^2 = 0$ to $q^2 = +\infty$. The reason for this cut at positive q^2 was already touched upon in Chapter I. Under some circumstances, one of the poles represents a bound state, a possibility that was also mentioned in Chapter I. The other pole, however, has to do with the potential, and in order to see how this comes about we must mention briefly analyticity properties one finds in a more complete treatment of f_o. We shall show that (2-4) represents a simple approximation to these analyticity properties. After studying the simple approximation in detail we shall return, at the end of this chapter and in later chapters, to a more careful consideration of the full analyticity properties of f_o.

The analyticity properties we are interested in have to do with a particle of mass M, scattering from the Yukawa potential:

$$V(r) = -\frac{\rho}{2M^2}\frac{e^{-mr}}{r} \quad . \tag{2-5}$$

This potential has a reasonable behavior at large distances and will generalize easily to relativistic scattering later on. The Yukawa potential can be Fourier-transformed to momentum space, where it gives the Born approximation f_B to the scattering amplitude:

$$f_B = \frac{\rho}{\pi}\frac{1}{\left[m^2 + 2q^2 - 2q^2 \cos\theta\right]} \quad . \tag{2-6}$$

The S-wave in Born approximation, f_{oB}, can be obtained from (2-6) by the partial-wave projection

$$f_{oB} = \frac{1}{2}\int_{-1}^{1} d\cos\theta \, f_B \, P_o(\cos\theta) = \frac{\rho}{4\pi q^2}\,\ell n\left(1 + \frac{4q^2}{m^2}\right) \quad . \tag{2-7}$$

Thus the Yukawa potential gives a cut in the kinetic energy variable $q^2/2M$, starting at $q^2 = -m^2/4$. The magnitude of the discontinuity increases with the strength of the potential, and the discontinuity comes closer to the physical threshold $q^2 = 0$ as the range of the potential $(1/m)$ is increased. This discontinuity together with corrections, to be discussed later, from iterations of the potential, is called the "left cut" (Fig. 2-1). In Born approximation, the left cut is the only discontinuity but in higher orders a "right cut" at the physical kinetic energies $q^2/2M = 0$ to ∞ also appears due to the opposite phases at $q^2 + i\epsilon$ and $q^2 - i\epsilon$, as explained in the Introduction.

Now the simplest approximation to the left cut is to replace it by a single pole $\lambda/(q^2 + a^2)$ where, crudely speaking, λ represents the strength of the potential and $1/a$ the range of the potential. There remains the problem of finding the right cut by iteration of the potential. For this purpose, it is convenient to write the amplitude as a quotient[7)]

$$f_o = \frac{N}{D} \quad , \tag{2-9}$$

where

$$N = \frac{\lambda}{q^2 + a^2} \tag{2-10}$$

contains the approximate left cut and D contains all of the right cut with no other singularities. D can therefore be represented by a Cauchy integral

$$D = \frac{1}{\pi} \int_0^{\infty} \frac{dq'^2}{q'^2 - q^2} \operatorname{Im} D\,(q'^2) \quad , \tag{2-11}$$

where we have used the fact that the discontinuity is purely imaginary, and have assumed that the integral converges. An advantage of writing the amplitude as a quotient in this way can be seen by combining

$$\text{Im } D = N \text{ Im } 1/f_0 \qquad (q^2 \geq 0) \tag{2-12}$$

with the "unitarity condition" that tells us the phase δ is real for elastic scattering:

$$\text{Im } 1/f_0 = \text{Im}\left[q \cot \delta - i\, q\right] = -q \qquad (q^2 \geq 0) \tag{2-13}$$

to give

$$\text{Im } D = -q\, N \qquad (q^2 \geq 0) \; . \tag{2-14}$$

We now use (2-14) in the Cauchy integral (2-11) and make the normalization $D(q^2 = -a^2) = 1$ by a subtraction:

$$D = 1 - \frac{(q^2 + a^2)}{\pi} \int_0^\infty \frac{dq'^2\, N(q'^2)\, q'}{(q'^2 + a^2)(q'^2 - q^2)} \; . \tag{2-15}$$

Explicit integration using the one-pole approximation to N (2-10) does converge and yields

$$D = 1 + \frac{\lambda}{2a} - \frac{\lambda}{a - i\, q} \; , \tag{2-16}$$

$$f_0 = \frac{N}{D} = \frac{1}{a^2 \left(\frac{1}{\lambda} - \frac{1}{2a}\right) + q^2 \left(\frac{1}{\lambda} + \frac{1}{2a}\right) - i\, q} \; . \tag{2-17}$$

The relation of the effective range approximation (2-4) to the full analytic structure of f_0 is now clear. It has the same structure as the one-pole approximation to the left cut (2-17):

i) Both have two poles in q, as well as a cut in q^2. One of the poles has now been identified with the potential term.

ii) Both contain two parameters.

iii) Both satisfy unitarity.

iv) Both are valid near threshold for a short-range potential. The reason the one-pole approximation is valid over only a limited energy range is that the left cut can look similar to a pole only over a limited region. If the force became longer range, the pole would have to come closer to threshold and the approximation would retain its validity in a more and more limited region.

For a given range of forces, one of the two poles in q is fixed at $q = i\,a$. It turns out that the other pole moves as the strength of the potential varies for a given range $1/a$. The positioning of poles in the q plane is illustrated in Fig. 2-2. Meanwhile, the q^2 plane exhibits a slightly more complicated, two-sheeted structure. A value of q,

$$q = |q|\, e^{i\theta} \quad , \tag{2-18}$$

corresponds to

$$q^2 = |q|^2\, e^{2i\theta} \quad , \tag{2-19}$$

so a rotation through $\theta = 2\pi$ in q corresponds to a rotation through 4π in q^2. The region $0 < \theta < \pi$ ($\mathrm{Im}\, q > 0$) transforms to the q^2 sheet pictured in Fig. 2-2, while $\mathrm{Im}\, q < 0$ goes onto a second sheet.

The first sheet is called the <u>physical sheet</u> because:

i) physical $q = |q| + i\epsilon$ is on it at ①.

ii) when the pole that moves as the potential strength varies appears on the first sheet, it has the significance of a physical bound state as described in the Introduction. Evidently, this is the sheet we were working on when we used the N/D method.

Now let us study the moving pole. The fixed pole was a pole of N (2-10); the moving pole is a zero of D (2-16). It is located at

$$D = 1 + \frac{\lambda}{2a} - \frac{\lambda}{a - i\,q} = 0 \quad , \tag{2-20}$$

which has the solution

$$q = i\,a \left[\frac{\lambda - 2a}{\lambda + 2a}\right] \quad . \tag{2-21}$$

So, as we vary the strength of interaction at fixed a, the pole moves as indicated in Fig. 2-2.

Consider the case $|\lambda| < 2a$. Here the pole lies on the second q^2 sheet. The amplitude can be rewritten

$$f_o = \frac{a^2\,(\frac{1}{\lambda} - \frac{1}{2a}) + q^2\,(\frac{1}{\lambda} + \frac{1}{2a}) + i\,q}{\left[a^2\,(\frac{1}{\lambda} - \frac{1}{2a}) + q^2\,(\frac{1}{\lambda} + \frac{1}{2a})\right]^2 + q^2}$$

$$= \frac{\cos\delta\,\sin\delta + i\,\sin^2\delta}{q} \quad . \tag{2-22}$$

Above threshold, q^2 is positive, and the coefficients of a^2 and q^2 are dominated by $1/\lambda$, so $\cos\delta \sin\delta$ has the sign of $(a^2 + q^2)1/\lambda$:

$$\lambda > 0 \rightarrow \delta > 0 \qquad \text{(attraction when } \lambda > 0)$$

$$\lambda < 0 \rightarrow \delta < 0 \qquad \text{(repulsion when } \lambda < 0) \quad .$$

The greater the interaction strength $|\lambda|$, the greater the phase shift. Note that $\cos\delta \sin\delta$ never vanishes so the phase shift never reaches 90° (Fig. 2-3).

As $\lambda \rightarrow 2a$, one finds

$$f_0\,(q^2 = 0) = \frac{1}{a^2\,(\frac{1}{\lambda} - \frac{1}{2a})} \rightarrow \infty \tag{2-23}$$

(i.e., the scattering length approaches ∞). At the same time, the moving pole is now nearing the physical sheet. We identify this phenomenon with a "virtual" or nearly bound state -- e.g., the singlet n-p state.

As λ passes 2a, the moving pole comes onto the physical sheet where it is interpreted as a physical bound state. The zero of $\operatorname{Re} f_0$ at

$$q^2 = a^2\left[\frac{\lambda - 2a}{\lambda + 2a}\right] \tag{2-24}$$

was negative below threshold for $\lambda < 2a$, but now moves above threshold for $\lambda > 2a$. It represents $\cos\delta = 0$ or $\delta = 90^\circ$. At threshold $f_0\,(q^2 = 0) = a^{-2}\left[\frac{1}{\lambda} - \frac{1}{2a}\right]^{-1}$ is now negative. So one finds the top curve in Fig. 2-3 -- e.g., triplet n-p scattering.

<u>Comment</u>: Only one bound state is possible in the present model. This is, of course, an unrealistic result of the one-pole approximation.

Comment: There are never any resonances no matter how attractive the potential may be. This is because the interaction (2-5) with $\lambda > 0$ is purely attractive. If there were a centrifugal barrier ($\ell > 0$) dominating at large r, or if the potential had a repulsive outer region, then a resonance could be "trapped" by the barrier above threshold.

Comment: One can work out the residue of the moving pole in the q^2 plane. One finds the residue

$$\lambda \left[\frac{\lambda - 2a}{\lambda + 2a}\right] \quad ; \tag{2-25}$$

the pole is at $q_B^2 = - a^2 \left[\frac{\lambda - 2a}{\lambda + 2a}\right]^2$. Such a pole in the energy variable corresponds to the familiar matrix element $<$ free S state | bound state $>$ $(E - E_{Bound})^{-1}$ $<$ bound state | free S state $>$, and the residue is related to the square of the overlap between bound state and free state. For a loosely bound state, the residue is supposed to reduce approximately to the square of the normalization of the asymptotic bound state wave function.[8] We can check this, writing $\psi \sim B \exp\left[- |q_B|\, r\right]$. Determine B by

$$\int_0^\infty \psi^2 \, dr = 1 = \frac{B^2}{2\,|q_B|} = \frac{B^2}{2a\left[\frac{\lambda - 2a}{\lambda + 2a}\right]} \quad . \tag{2-26}$$

Thus we have

$$B^2 = 2a \left\lfloor\frac{\lambda - 2a}{\lambda + 2a}\right\rfloor \tag{2-27}$$

which is the same as the residue (2-25) for weakly bound states ($\lambda \sim 2a$).

<u>Application</u>: From the binding energy of the deuteron and the range of the n-p force, one gets a moderately successful estimate for the residue of the deuteron pole in ^3S, n-p scattering.

Finally, consider $\lambda < -2a$. As $|\lambda| \to \infty$, $f_o\ (q^2 = 0)$ approaches $-2/a$ and the cross section $\sigma(q^2 = 0) = 4\pi\ |f_o|^2$ approaches $16\pi\ a^{-2}$. Identifying σ with $4\pi R^2$, we find $R = 2/a$, verifying that the inverse distance to the pole is a measure of range of interaction.

In general, at $\lambda < -2a$, we find $f_o\ (q^2 = 0) < 0$, as was the case for $\lambda > 2a$, and δ passes through 90° (Fig. 2-3). This looks just like the behavior associated with a bound state. But the interaction is repulsive ($\lambda < 0$, so that $\delta < 0$ to first order in λ). The effective range approximation has evidently developed some anomalous features here, for reasons we shall examine. The pole in this pathological case is called a <u>ghost</u>.

To understand ghosts, we must study the connection between moving poles on the physical sheet, and unitarity. The unitarity bound of $f = e^{i\delta} \sin \delta/q$ is $|f|_{max} = q^{-1}$ when q^2 is real and positive. Now $N = \lambda/(q^2 + a^2)$ gives the amplitude to first order in the interaction strength λ. The quantity

$$\frac{N}{|f|_{max}} = \frac{\lambda\ q}{q^2 + a^2} \qquad (2\text{-}28)$$

is maximal at $q^2 = a^2$, where it has the value $\lambda/2a$. So $|N|$ exceeds $|f|_{max}$ precisely when poles appear on the left cut. A glance at f_o shows that this is also precisely the point where f_o can no longer be expanded in powers of λ on the physical sheet:

$$f_o\,(q^2 = 0) = \frac{\lambda}{a^2\,(1 - \frac{\lambda}{2a})} \quad . \tag{2-29}$$

The connection is obvious since when first order in λ exceeds the unitarity bound, a power series application of unitarity would not be expected to converge. Incidentally, the fact that our solution continues to satisfy unitarity when λ is outside its circle of convergence was one of the leading motivations for writing the amplitude as an N/D ratio of power series in λ.

The Cauchy integral on the physical sheet, in the presence of either a bound state or ghost at $q^2 = q_B^2$, takes the form

$$f_o = \frac{-\lambda\left[\frac{\lambda - 2a}{\lambda + 2a}\right]}{q^2 - q_B^2} + \frac{\lambda}{q^2 + a^2} + \frac{1}{\pi}\int_0^\infty \frac{dq'^2\ \mathrm{Im}\ f_o}{q'^2 - q^2} \quad . \tag{2-30}$$

At $\lambda > 2a$, the positive λ represents an attraction and the residue of the bound state is negative. So the bound state tends to restore the unitarity bound which was violated by the fixed pole. At $\lambda < 2a$, the negative λ represents a repulsion and the residue of the ghost at q_B^2 is positive. So again, the ghost tends to restore the unitarity bound which was violated by the fixed pole at $-a^2$. As λ approaches $-\infty$, the ghost gets closer to the fixed pole and its residue approaches $-\lambda$ in order to cancel the fixed pole. We conclude that the moving pole appears on the physical sheet when the interaction gets too strong; its role is to restore unitarity.

Do ghosts have a more fundamental significance? At one time, Pauli and others thought ghosts should be a general feature of a correct field theory. They were to introduce an indefinite metric which would eliminate divergence problems.[9,10] Why an indefinite metric? We saw that a ghost has a residue of opposite sign from a proper bound state. The sign of the bound state residue is related to the "positive norm" of a physical state -- in our case we passed from a two-particle state to a bound state and back again, and such a squared process has a definite sign (2-27). The ghost -- with opposite sign -- has a negative norm, and an indefinite metric is just the possibility of norms of either sign. How can an indefinite metric eliminate divergence problems? Divergence problems always imply a violation of unitarity. We saw that a ghost restores unitarity in the case of a strong repulsion. It averted a divergence which would otherwise have occurred.

But do ghosts really appear in potential theory? For those potentials which lead to a Mandelstam representation, there are no ghosts. Ghosts appear only when one makes some approximation which mutilates the representation -- as the one pole left cut did in our case. Of course, the ghost we found is only one of the possible varieties, corresponding to different mutilations.

To cite an example, Bjorken and Goldberg[11] studied the S-wave scattered by the exponential potential $V(r) = - \lambda \exp(-mr)$, which is exactly soluble. The left cut is a series of poles (Fig. 2-4): the residue of the pole nearest the origin is proportional to λ, the residue of the second pole is proportional to λ^2, and so on (if one thinks of the potential as exchanging mass m each time it acts, then mass nm is exchanged when the particle acts n times (λ^n), and the pole appears at larger $|q^2|$ -- i.e., shorter range -- as the exchanged mass increases). For an attraction ($\lambda > 0$), successive terms in the Born series add as usual. For a repulsion, successive terms in the Born series tend to cancel.

Bjorken and Goldberg tried a one-pole approximation and found a ghost for strong repulsion; of course, it was just simulating the attractive effect of the other singularities which should have been there. Then they tried a two-pole approximation; ghosts could still appear if the repulsion was strong enough, but this time they had smaller residues and were further out on the left cut, because the second pole was already in the right direction to restore unitarity. In other words, the two-pole approximation worked for a wider range of energies and potential strengths.

As for the question of ghosts in field theory, much of the speculation was based on the Lee model.[12)] Although this model was originally presented in very different terms than effective range theory, it turns out to have essentially the same analyticity properties.* In particular, the left cut was originally approximated by a simple pole, while

*In fact, many papers where model problems are solved exactly in one or more coupled channels owe their simplicity to this type of analytic structure.

unitarity was enforced on the right cut. A ghost naturally resulted. Since the ghost we have studied in non-relativistic theory results from inadequate approximations, and can be improved by improving the method of calculation, it becomes plausible that ghosts in relativistic theories such as the Lee model could also be removed by improved treatment of the left cut.

Next, we investigate the rate at which phase shifts can decrease in the effective range model. The results will check with general conclusions of Wigner, who found that[13)]

$$\frac{d\delta_o}{dq} > -(\text{range of forces}) \quad , \tag{2-31}$$

provided we make a reasonable interpretation of "range".

To indicate the underlying physics, we repeat a simple argument from Wigner's paper. Consider a scattering center of radius R, such that the incident particle behaves like a free particle outside a sphere of this radius; consider an incident beam which is the superposition of two monoenergetic beams of energy $\hbar(\nu + \nu')$ and $\hbar(\nu - \nu')$, respectively. The corresponding wave numbers are denoted by $q + q'$ and $q - q'$. Hence

$$\psi_{in} = r^{-1}\left[e^{-i(q+q')r-i(\nu+\nu')t} + e^{-i(q-q')r-i(\nu-\nu')t}\right] \quad . \tag{2-32}$$

Both q' and ν' are infinitesimally small so that (2-32) is a substitute for a wave packet, the center of which is at the point where the two spherical waves of (2-32) are in phase:

$$q' r + \nu' t = 0 \quad . \tag{2-33}$$

The velocity of the particle is

$$V = -\frac{\nu'}{q'} \quad (\rightarrow \ -\frac{d\nu}{dq}) \quad . \tag{2-34}$$

If $\delta + \delta'$ and $\delta - \delta'$ are the phase shifts corresponding to the energy values $\hbar(\nu + \nu')$ and $\hbar(\nu - \nu')$, the outgoing wave will be

$$\psi_{out} = r^{-1}\Big[e^{i(q+q')r-i(\nu+\nu')t+2i(\delta+\delta')} + e^{i(q-q')r-i(\nu-\nu')t+2i(\delta-\delta')}\Big] \quad . \tag{2-35}$$

The two waves of (2-35) are in phase when

$$q' r - \nu' t + 2\delta' = 0 \quad , \tag{2-36}$$

i.e., where

$$r = -\frac{2\delta'}{q'} + (\frac{\nu'}{q'})\, t \quad (\rightarrow \ -\frac{2d\delta}{dq} + (\frac{d\nu}{dq})\ t\ ) \quad . \tag{2-37}$$

Evidently, the outgoing wave is retarded by a distance $2\, d\delta/dq$, due to the action of the scattering center. Positive retardation corresponds to trapping of the incoming wave by the scattering center; causality places no limit on such retardation. But causality does prohibit the wave from arriving too far in advance; classically the retardation cannot be more negative than -2R. This gives the limit

$$\frac{d\delta}{dq} \gtrsim -R \tag{2-38}$$

which, Wigner shows, remains approximately valid for wave mechanics.

Turning to the effective range formula, we can rewrite $f = e^{i\delta} \sin \delta/q$ as

$$\delta = \frac{1}{2i} \ln \left[2\, i\, q\, f + 1 \right] \quad . \tag{2-39}$$

The explicit effective range formula (2-17) gives

$$\frac{d\delta}{dq} = \frac{\lambda \left\{ a^2 \left(1 - \frac{\lambda}{2a}\right) - q^2 \left(1 + \frac{\lambda}{2a}\right) \right\}}{\left[a^2 \left(1 - \frac{\lambda}{2a}\right) + q^2 \left(1 + \frac{\lambda}{2a}\right) \right]^2 + \lambda^2 q^2} \tag{2-40}$$

which can be studied in various cases. When $|\lambda|$ approaches ∞,

$$\frac{d\delta}{dq} \rightarrow \frac{-2a}{a^2 + q^2} \geq -\frac{2}{a} \tag{2-41}$$

in agreement with the previous interpretation of 2/a as the range of the potential. When $-\infty < \lambda < 2a$, $d\delta/dq > -2/a$. When $\lambda = 2a\,(1 + \epsilon)$ with $\epsilon > 0$ (weakly bound states), $d\delta/dq$ approaches a minimum $-\frac{2(1+\epsilon)}{a\epsilon}$ as $q \rightarrow 0$. Here, $d\delta/dq$ can be very large and negative.

Example: The triplet n-p phase shift falls rapidly through 90°, starting from 180° at threshold.

Interpretation: A weakly bound state provides a long-range structure for low-energy particles to jump into virtually. At large r, the bound state wave function is $\psi \sim \exp\,(-\,|q_B|\,r)$ where

$$|q_B| = a \left[\frac{\lambda - 2a}{\lambda + 2a} \right] \simeq \frac{a\epsilon}{2(1+\epsilon)} \quad ; \tag{2-42}$$

thus the effective radius is $|q_B|^{-1} \simeq \frac{2(1 + \epsilon)}{a\epsilon}$, which is just the radius indicated in the weakly bound case. The Wigner principle still holds but the range is now interpreted in terms of the bound state extending outside the original potential. The corresponding statement for the complex plane is that the bound state pole is closer to the physical region of $q^2 \geq 0$ than is the original pole representing the potential, and effectively gives a longer range.

Let us turn now to some further properties of scattering, still confining our attention to the S-state for simplicity. The amplitude f and the S-matrix are defined by

$$f = \frac{e^{2i\delta} - 1}{2\,i\,q} \tag{2-43}$$

and

$$S = e^{2i\delta} \quad . \tag{2-44}$$

Therefore, we have

$$S = 2\,i\,q\,f + 1 \quad . \tag{2-45}$$

From the explicit expression (2-17) for f, we find

$$S = \frac{a^2\left(\frac{1}{\lambda} - \frac{1}{2a}\right) + q^2\left(\frac{1}{\lambda} + \frac{1}{2a}\right) + i\,q}{a^2\left(\frac{1}{\lambda} - \frac{1}{2a}\right) + q^2\left(\frac{1}{\lambda} + \frac{1}{2a}\right) - i\,q} \quad . \tag{2-46}$$

We see explicitly that

$$S(q) = \frac{1}{S(-q)} \tag{2-47}$$

and

$$S(q^*) = \frac{1}{S^*(q)} \tag{2-48}$$

where $S^*(q)$ means: take the complex conjugate of q and of the functional dependence on q. These relations are general (for a good discussion, see Reference 14). To prove the first relation, write the asymptotic wave function for momentum q:

$$u(q) \sim e^{-iqr} - S(q)\, e^{iqr} \tag{2-49}$$

and -q:

$$u(-q) \sim e^{-i(-q)r} - S(-q)\, e^{i(-q)r} \quad . \tag{2-50}$$

The Schrödinger equation is the same for q and -q, so the asymptotic parts of $u(q)$ and $u(-q)$ are proportional:

$$u(-q) \propto \frac{-u(+q)}{S(q)} = -\frac{1}{S(q)}\, e^{-iqr} + e^{iqr} \quad . \tag{2-51}$$

By comparison of (2-50) and (2-51), (2-47) is proved. Equation (2-48) can be established by similar arguments.

Combining (2-47) and (2-48), we obtain

$$S(q) = S^*(-q^*) \tag{2-52}$$

or, in other words,

$$S(q_R + i\, q_I) = S^*(-\, q_R + i\, q_I) \quad .$$

If S has a pole at $q_R + i\, q_I$, (2-52) implies that S also has a pole at $q_R - i\, q_I$, and (2-47) then implies zeros at $q_R \pm i\, q_I$.

<u>Example I</u>. In the effective range formula, S only has one moving pole, which must lie on the imaginary axis because of the reflection principle. According to (2-48), a zero moves conjugate to the pole.

When the zero reaches the origin, it overlaps the pole (otherwise $\exp(2i\delta)$ could not be finite at threshold). From another point of view, as the binding energy of a bound state approaches zero, its wave function extends to ∞. The coefficient of the asymptotic wave function must then vanish to keep the wave function normalizable, so the residue of the bound state pole vanishes (2-27).

Example II. A typical resonance situation is pictured in Fig. 2-5. The number of poles is now increases; just as the potential must now be more complicated to provide both an attractive well and outside barrier to hold the resonance in. If any one of the poles or zeroes exists, (2-47) and (2-48) imply the other three. The situation in the q^2 plane is illustrated in Fig. 2-6. The positioning of the pole on the unphysical sheet gives a Breit-Wigner form

$$S \sim \frac{1}{q^2 - q_R^2 + i\,\Gamma} \quad , \tag{2-53}$$

where $\Gamma > 0$ has the correct sign. The pole cannot appear on the physical sheet because that would give the wrong sign, corresponding to a state decaying backwards in time.

As the attractive potential responsible for the resonance is increased, the resonance moves towards threshold, with Γ decreasing because less phase space is available to decay into (Fig. 2-5). When the resonance reaches $q = 0$, it is overlapped by the zeroes, again ensuring the correct threshold behavior. A further increase in potential leads to a bound state; one pole moves up the imaginary q axis and the other must move down to stay off the physical sheet.

Why couldn't the moving singularities be cuts instead of poles? Suppose a branch point is located on the unphysical sheet* ($\mathrm{Im}\ q < 0$). An inverted pole becomes a zero, but an inverted branch point remains a branch point; therefore (2-47) implies that a branch point also occurs on the physical sheet ($\mathrm{Im}\ q > 0$). But as far as is known, moving singularities do not occur on the physical sheet except for bound state poles at $\mathrm{Re}\ q = 0$.

With the aid of the symmetry properties of S, we can now discuss the N/D method in more generality. As we shall see later, the Mandelstam representation for a finite range potential gives fixed cuts along the positive and negative $\mathrm{Im}\ q$ axes, extending as far as the origin. In the q^2 plane there is also the branch cut from $q^2 = 0$ to $q^2 = \infty$ (Fig. 2-1). In addition, there may be moving poles of the type we have investigated already. The same singularities occur in f. From (2-43), (2-44), and (2-52), we see that f also satisfies

$$f^*(q) = f(-q^*) \tag{2-54}$$

and therefore

$$f^*(q^2) = f(q^{2*}) \quad . \tag{2-55}$$

The right (R) and left (L) branch points occur at real q^2, so the cuts can be taken entirely along the real axis. Equation (2-55) then ensures that the discontinuities across them are purely imaginary and the Cauchy representation for f takes the simple form

---

*The argument here is due to M. Froissart, private communication.

$$f = \frac{1}{\pi} \int_L \frac{\mathrm{Im}\, f\,(q'^2)\, dq'^2}{q'^2 - q^2 - i\epsilon}$$

$$+ \frac{1}{\pi} \int_R \frac{\mathrm{Im}\, f\,(q'^2)\, dq'^2}{q'^2 - q^2 - i\epsilon} \tag{2-56}$$

plus possible poles and subtractions. Now express f by $f = N/D$. It is consistent with (2-55) to give N and D the properties

$$N^*(q^2) = N(q^{2*}) \tag{2-57}$$

$$D^*(q^2) = D(q^{2*}) \quad . \tag{2-58}$$

If we define N to be analytic except on the left cut of f, and D to be analytic except on the right cut, their Cauchy representations then simplify to

$$N = \frac{1}{\pi} \int_L \frac{dq'^2\, \mathrm{Im}\, N\,(q'^2)}{q'^2 - q^2} \tag{2-59}$$

and

$$D = \frac{1}{\pi} \int_R \frac{dq'^2\, \mathrm{Im}\, D\,(q'^2)}{q'^2 - q^2} \tag{2-60}$$

plus possible subtractions. On the left cut

$$\mathrm{Im}\, N = D\, \mathrm{Im}\, f_o \tag{2-61}$$

and on the right cut

$$\mathrm{Im}\, D = N\, \mathrm{Im}\, \frac{1}{f_o} \quad . \tag{2-62}$$

The relation $\mathrm{Im}\, f_o^{-1} = -q$ (2-13) applies in general on the upper lip of the right cut. Thus we can write the coupled equations

$$N(q^2) = \frac{1}{\pi} \int_L \frac{dq'^2\, D(q'^2)\, \text{Im } f(q'^2)}{q'^2 - q^2} \tag{2-63}$$

$$D(q^2) = 1 - \frac{q^2 - q_o^2}{\pi} \int_R \frac{dq'^2\, q'\, N(q')}{(q'^2 - q^2)(q'^2 - q_o^2)} \tag{2-64}$$

where we have taken advantage of the freedom in normalization of D by setting $D(q_o^2) = 1$ and making a subtraction at this point. The approximation made in effective range theory on the left cut is

$$\text{Im } f(q'^2) = - \pi \lambda \delta (q'^2 + a^2) \tag{2-65}$$

so that

$$N = \frac{\lambda D(-a^2)}{q^2 + a^2} \quad . \tag{2-66}$$

The simplest normalization is $D(-a^2) = 1$; i.e., $-a^2 = q_o^2$.

Exercise: In cases where the effective potential is known, the left cut can be derived from it by methods to be discussed in connection with the Mandelstam representation; the left cut can then be approximated to any desired degree of accuracy by a sequence of poles. Show that if the left cut is approximated by a finite number of poles,

$$\text{Im } f (q'^2) = \pi \sum_i \lambda_i \delta (q'^2 + a_i^2) \quad , \tag{2-67}$$

then (2-63) and (2-64) can still be solved in closed form.

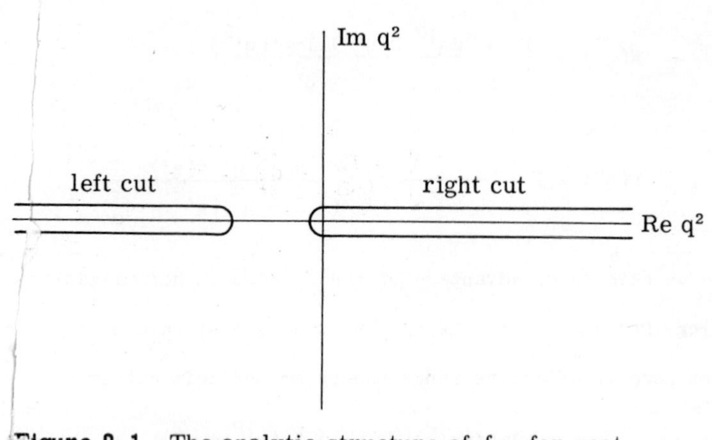

Figure 2-1 The analytic structure of f_0, for scattering from a Yukawa potential.

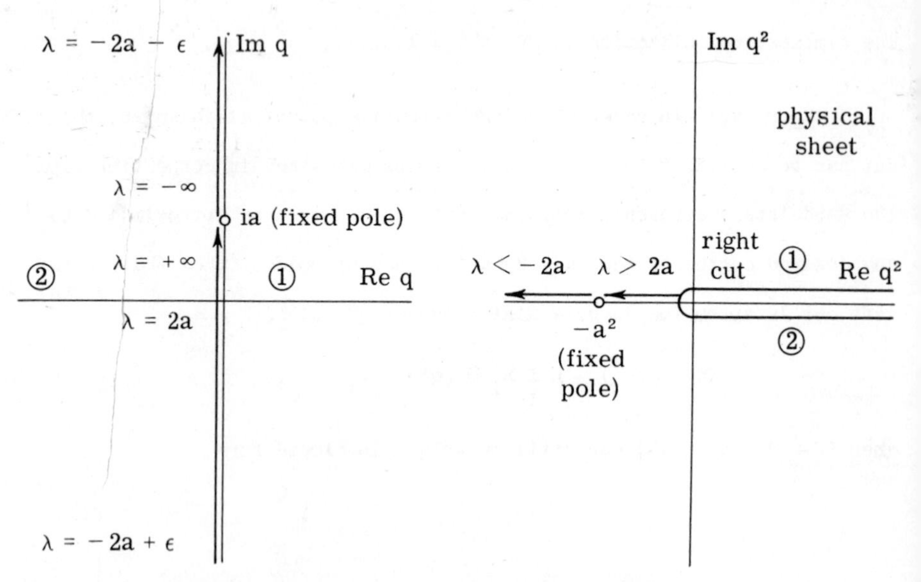

Figure 2-2 The path of the moving pole in the q and q^2 planes, for the effective range approximation. Position (1) at $q = \text{Re } q + i\epsilon$ ($\epsilon > 0$) represents physical scattering.

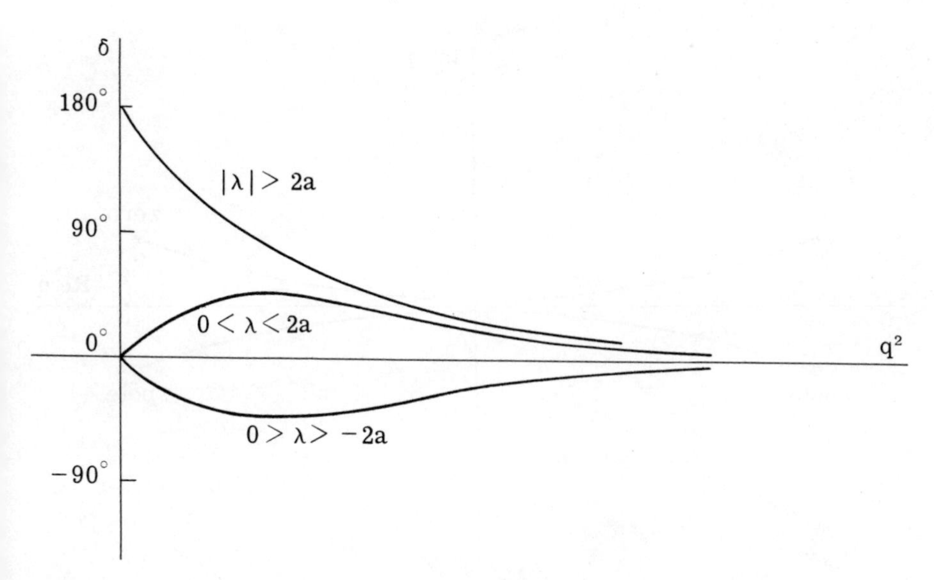

Figure 2-3 Effective range approximation: behavior of the phase shift.

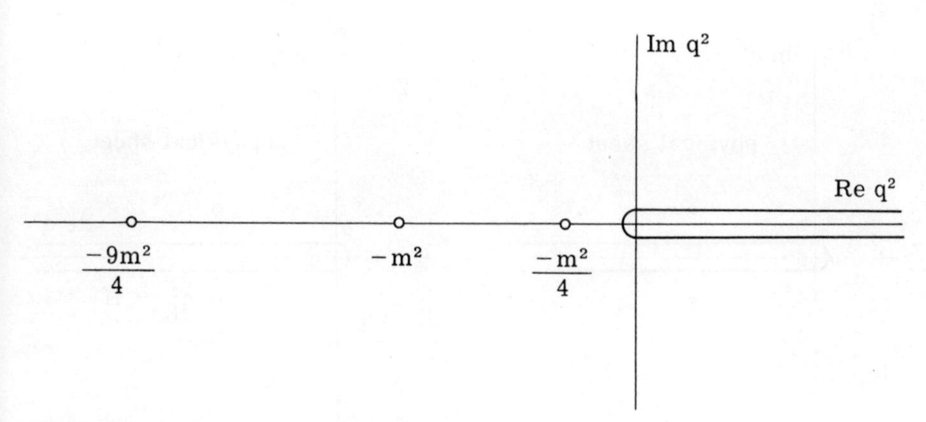

Figure 2-4 Location of singularities in the q^2 plane for scattering from an exponential potential.

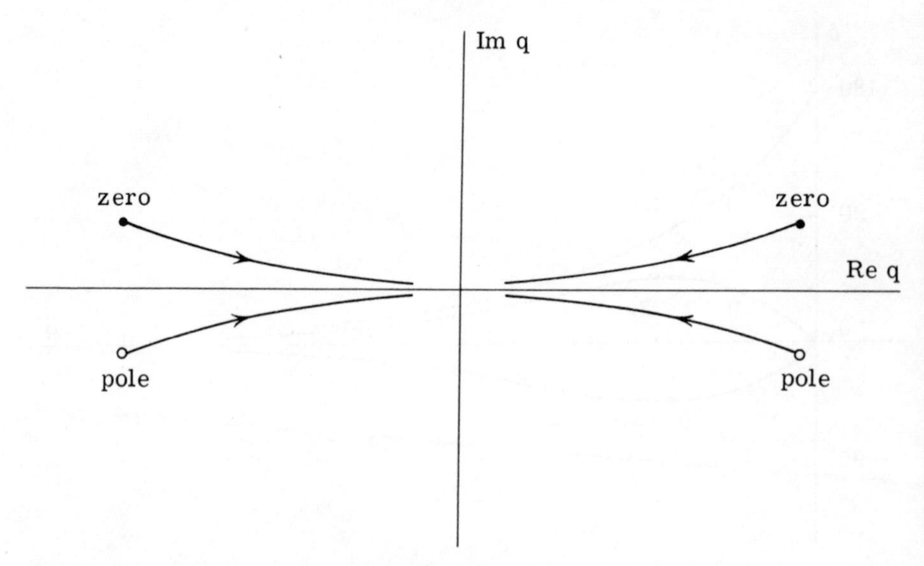

Figure 2-5 Movement of resonance poles and zeroes in the q plane as the coupling strength is increased.

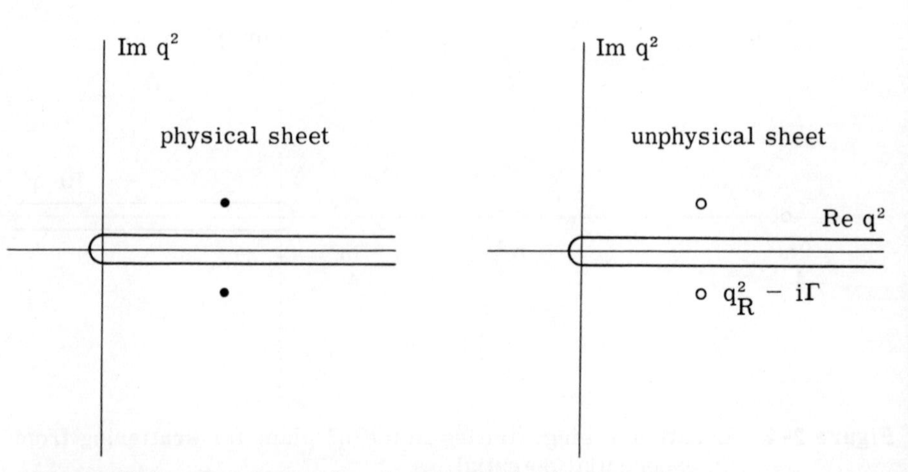

Figure 2-6 The physical and unphysical q^2 sheets for a resonance.

III. THE AMBIGUITY OF CASTILLEJO, DALITZ, AND DYSON, AND LEVINSON'S THEOREM

The N/D method is subject to an ambiguity, which was first emphasized by Castillejo, Dalitz, and Dyson.[15] One form of the ambiguity is that whereas new cuts in D would be inconsistent with the analyticity of f, poles can be added to D without adding any singularity to f in the physical region. Another aspect of the ambiguity is that the asymptotic behavior of N and D at large q^2 is not determined by the asymptotic behavior of their ratio N/D. Of course, the Schrödinger equation has a unique solution, so it must supply enough additional information to overcome these ambiguities. But this is not the case in strong interaction physics, where the non-relativistic equations are not applicable. In fact, there is a highly important physical possibility which was absent from our previous discussion of the N/D method: There may exist a particle with $J = 0$ which is stable in the absence of interaction, but decays when interactions are turned on. Such a particle would provide a resonant intermediate state. If it lies below threshold, it would remain stable in the presence of interaction.

We now wish to show that the two forms of mathematical ambiguity are equivalent, and that they express the physical possibility that stable particles are present when the interaction is turned off.

Consider the addition of a pole in D (i.e., a zero in f):

$$D \to 1 - \frac{(q^2 - q_o^2)}{\pi} \int_R \frac{dq'^2 \, N(q'^2) \, q'}{(q'^2 - q_o^2)(q'^2 - q^2)} + \frac{C}{q_p^2 - q^2} \equiv D_o + \frac{C}{q_p^2 - q^2} . \quad (3\text{-}1$$

This pole, a so-called CDD pole, has two parameters -- its residue and position. If the residue is sufficiently weak, D_o and the pole term interfere to give D a zero* somewhere near q_p^2. A zero of D is a pole of f, and poles of f have a plausible physical interpretation only under certain conditions. For example:

(a) A pole of f on the physical sheet, Re $q^2 > 0$, corresponds to a resonance of negative width decaying backward in time, which must be rejected.

(b) A pole of f on the physical sheet, at real negative q^2 in the gap between right and left cuts, is interpreted as a stable particle. This is the only position for a pole on the physical sheet with a well-established physical interpretation.

(c) A pole of f on the unphysical sheet is interpreted as a resonance or virtual state.

As the residue C is reduced to zero, the pole of f moves to q_p^2. If q_p^2 is real, the physical interpretation is that a particle with real mass exists at $q^2 = q_p^2$, before the interaction is turned on. When the interaction is turned on, this particle undergoes a mass shift, as evidenced by the movement of the pole. For particles lying

---

*This follows from the fact that D_o is constant in a sufficiently small region near q_p^2.

below threshold, the mass shift is real; if the particle lies above threshold, the mass shift is complex because the particle can decay. We reject complex q_p^2 (i.e., complex "bare mass") for lack of a good physical interpretation.

Note the distinction between the pole associated with q_p^2, and the pole we encountered in the effective range model. The former represents a stable physical particle when the coupling C is "turned off"; the latter can be interpreted as a bound state only when the interaction strength λ is increased to a definite non-zero value (resonances also become possible if a repulsive barrier is at hand, but again they appear only when the coupling attains a certain strength). We shall use the term "elementary particle" when referring to the first type of pole, and "composite particle" when discussing the second type which has its origin in the interaction.

Either type of particle can be stable (q^2 real and negative) or unstable (q^2 complex and on the second sheet). From this point of view, there may be no essential difference between the eight stable baryons N, Λ, Σ, Ξ, and the many baryon resonances. All of them may be composite, or some of them -- both stable and unstable -- may be elementary. Thus the number eight may have no mystic significance whatever.

Now we can multiply both N and D by $(q_p^2 - q^2)$ without changing f. This step removes the CDD pole from D and inserts the zero at $q^2 = q_p^2$ directly into N. At large positive q^2, $f = e^{i\delta} \sin \delta/q$

is bounded by q^{-1}. Suppose , for example, that $f \sim q^{-1}$ at large $|q|$, $N \sim q^{-1}$, and $D \sim 1$ before we multiply through by $(q^2 - q_p^2)$. The dispersion relations (2-63), (3-1) for N and D then converge as previously written. But after multiplication by $(q_p^2 - q^2)$, $N \sim q$ and $D \sim q^2$, and subtractions are required. For example, we may write

$$N = C_1 + \frac{q^2 - q_1^2}{\pi} \int_L \frac{dq'^2\, D(q'^2)\, \mathrm{Im}\, f(q'^2)}{(q'^2 - q^2)(q'^2 - q_1^2)} \quad , \tag{3-2}$$

$$D = 1 + C_2(q^2 - q_o^2) - \frac{(q^2 - q_o^2)^2}{\pi} \int_R \frac{dq'^2\, N(q'^2)\, q'}{(q'^2 - q^2)(q'^2 - q_o^2)^2} \quad . \tag{3-3}$$

The two parameters originally introduced into f by the CDD pole were C and q_p^2. After N and D are multiplied by $(q_p^2 - q^2)$, the same parameters appear as the position of the zero in N, and the value of D at $q^2 = q_p^2$, but the subtraction constants C_1 and C_2 form an equivalent pair of parameters. The connection between the arbitrariness of poles in D, and the arbitrariness of asymptotic behavior of N and D, is thus established. The lack of arbitrariness in non-relativistic potential theory is due to the absence of elementary particles in the ordinary treatment of that theory.

Now let us insert a CDD pole explicitly into the effective range formula:

$$N = \frac{\lambda}{q^2 + a^2} \quad , \tag{3-4}$$

$$D = 1 - \frac{(q^2+a^2)}{\pi} \int_0^\infty \frac{dq'^2\, q'\, \lambda}{(q'^2-q^2)(q'^2+a^2)} + \frac{C}{q_p^2 - q^2}$$

$$= 1 + \lambda \left[\frac{1}{2a} - \frac{1}{a-iq}\right] + \frac{C}{q_p^2 - q^2} \quad . \tag{3-5}$$

The D function now has two more zeroes than formerly. At a zero of D, the condition $\operatorname{Im} D = 0$ must be satisfied. If we set $q = q_R + iq_I$, this implies that either $q_R = 0$ as before or

$$\frac{\lambda}{2q_I\, C} = \frac{(a + q_I)^2 + q_R^2}{\left[q_p^2 - q_R^2 + q_I^2\right]^2 + 4\, q_R^2\, q_I^2} \quad . \tag{3-6}$$

The first relation, $q_R = 0$, is satisfied by one pole which for small C behaves essentially like the pole we had for $C = 0$. The second relation is satisfied by a conjugate pair of poles. When the second relation applies, λ/C is negative because the right side is positive definite and we have imposed the physical requirement that the zero be on the second sheet ($q_I < 0$). Also note that $f = 0$ (i.e., the phase shift is zero or a multiple of π) at $q^2 = q_p^2$. With these points in mind, we can work out the phase shifts for small C in various cases (Fig. 3-1).

In each resonance associated with a CDD pole, the phase shift rises through 90°. This is normal and was ensured by the requirement $q_I \leq 0$ at the zero of D (when $q_R \neq 0$). The plots of $|f|^2$ against q^2 are more complicated than for normal resonances. Of course, this is a consequence of adding two parameters to the description of the resonance. For small C, the phase shift passes through $\delta = 0$ or π near $\delta = \pi/2$, and Chew[16)] has proposed the use of this property as an experimental test for CDD poles. Unfortunately, C could be large, or the detailed dynamics might cause a zero of f near a resonance even without a CDD pole.

In all cases (2-17) and (3-4), (3-5) satisfy the relation

$$\delta(\infty) - \delta(0) = \pi (N_B - N_A) \qquad (3\text{-}7)$$

where N_B is the number of stable (elementary) particles <u>before</u> the interactions are turned on, and N_A is the number of stable elementary or composite particles <u>after</u> the interactions are turned on.* This relation is known as Levinson's Theorem.[17)]

We shall give a physical argument for Levinson's theorem in non-relativistic wave mechanics, and then a discussion in S-matrix language which can be extended to the relativistic case. For the physical argument, we assume a finite range potential, and we count the S-states in a finite spherical box centered on the spherically symmetric potential. The total number of S-states equals the number of stable S-states plus the number of scattering S-states for which the asymptotic wave function

$$\psi \sim \sin (q\, r + \delta_o (q)) \qquad (3\text{-}8)$$

vanishes on the spherical boundary $r = R$. The condition for this to happen is

$$q\, R + \delta_o (q) = n\, \pi \qquad n = 0, 1, 2, \ldots \qquad (3\text{-}9)$$

---

*A ghost has the same effect as a stable particle.

Evidently,

$$\frac{dn}{dq} = \frac{1}{\pi} (R + \frac{d\delta_o}{dq}) \qquad (3\text{-}10)$$

so the number of scattering states increases when δ_o increases, and vice versa. Now if we switch on the potential adiabatically, the total number of S-states remains constant. Any change in the number of stable states must be made up by a change in the number of scattering states. Integration of (3-10) gives the change in scattering states.

$$\Delta n = \int_0^\infty (\frac{dn}{dq} - \frac{R}{\pi})\, dq = \frac{1}{\pi} (\delta(\infty) - \delta(0)) \quad . \qquad (3\text{-}11)$$

The change in the number of stable states is just the negative of this in agreement with Levinson's result (we have assumed the quantities appearing in (3-11) are finite and the limit $\delta(q)$ as $q \to \infty$ exists).

In order to extend the discussion to the relativistic case, a more abstract argument based on the S-matrix is helpful.* Consider the D function

$$D(q^2) = 1 + \frac{q^2 - q_o^2}{\pi} \int_0^\infty dq'^2 \frac{\text{Im } D(q'^2)}{(q'^2 - q^2)(q'^2 - q_o^2)} \quad . \qquad (3\text{-}12)$$

If there are no CDD poles, it is known for the Schrödinger equation and will be confirmed in our later discussion of the Mandelstam representation that the potential completely determines the amplitude with no

*This argument is due in considerable part to M. Froissart, private discussion. A different but physically equivalent method has been developed by R. Omnes in Reference 18.

arbitrary constants appearing. The representation (3-12) indeed converges with no arbitrary subtraction constants when $D \alpha (q^2)^r$, $r < 1$, at large q^2. We have seen that CDD poles at q_p^2 introduce arbitrary constants, and that when the poles are removed by multiplying through with $(q^2 - q_p^2)$ the arbitrariness takes the form of N_B arbitrary subtraction constants in D, where N_B is the number of CDD poles. The asymptotic behavior of D is now $D \alpha (q^2)^{r+N_B}$. Zeroes of D at q_B^2 on the physical sheet can similarly be removed by dividing through* by $(q^2 - q_B^2)$. The number of such zeroes is the number of bound states and stable elementary particles, previously called N_A. We have now constructed a new D function with defining properties:

(a) no poles or zeroes on the physical sheet.

(b) $D \alpha (q^2)^{r+N_B-N_A}$ as $q^2 \to \infty$ $(r < 1)$.

(c) phase $\mp\delta$ at $q^2 \pm i\epsilon$ on the right cut (since $N/D = e^{\pm i\delta} \sin \delta/q$ and N is real at $q^2 + i\epsilon$ on the right cut).

Omnes[19] has introduced a function

$$D' = \exp\left[- \frac{q^2 - q_0^2}{\pi} \int_0^\infty \frac{dq'^2 \, \delta(q')}{(q'^2 - q_0^2)(q'^2 - q^2 - i\epsilon)} \right] \tag{3-13}$$

which explicitly satisfies properties (a) (we define $\delta(0) = 0$ to avoid zeroes or poles which would occur at threshold if $\delta(0) = n\pi$) and (c), and can be normalized to one at the same place as D. The asymptotic behavior of D' is given by

---

*Note that dividing through by $q^2 - q_B^2$ places the pole of f in N. This is a common practice in pion-nucleon scattering, where the nucleon pole is often considered to be "given" and placed in N.

$$\lim_{q^2 \to \infty} D'(q^2) = \exp\left[\frac{\delta(\infty)}{\pi} \ell n\, q^2 + \text{const}\right] \tag{3-14}$$

$$\alpha\, (q^2)^{\delta(\infty)/\pi} \quad .$$

We can now form the ratio $R = D'/D$, which has asymptotic behavior $R \sim (q^2)^m$ (since both D and D' are bounded by a finite power). The phase on the right cut cancels out of the ratio. Therefore, the ratio is analytic and has no zeroes on poles at finite q^2. Consider the contour integral

$$\oint \frac{R'(q^2)\, dq^2}{R(q^2)} = m \oint \frac{dq^2}{q^2} = 2\pi i\, m \tag{3-15}$$

taken around a circle of large q^2. The integral vanishes because it encloses no singularities or zeroes of R. Therefore, $m = 0$, the equivalence of D and D' is established, and

$$\frac{\delta(\infty) - \delta(0)}{\pi} = r + N_B - N_A \quad , \quad (r < 1) \tag{3-16}$$

which is the "weak Levinson's theorem" that applies even in the relativistic case. Froissart[20] has generalized the method to include inelastic scattering. In non-relativistic scattering, one has enough additional information to show that $r = 0$, but no one has been able to extend this result to the general case.* For this reason and because

---

*Phase shifts for the Klein-Gordan and Dirac equations do not approach multiples of π as $q^2 \to \infty$, so $r \neq 0$ in this case. Of course, these equations are not physically valid at high energies -- where pairs and other particles can be produced.

of practical difficulties in measuring individual phase shifts at high energies, Levinson's Theorem has not provided a practical test for elementary particles in the past.

We close this discussion of partial-wave dispersion relations by considering the ℓth partial wave:

$$f_\ell = e^{i\delta_\ell} \frac{\sin \delta_\ell}{q} \quad , \tag{3-17}$$

where $\delta_\ell \sim q^{2\ell+1}$ at small q. If we set up the N/D method for f_ℓ in the same manner as for f_o, the threshold zero $f_\ell \sim q^{2\ell}$ is not guaranteed to come out right except for the S-wave. This difficulty can be removed by considering the function

$$g_\ell = e^{i\delta_\ell} \frac{\sin \delta_\ell}{q^{2\ell+1}} \quad , \tag{3-18}$$

which ensures proper behavior at threshold. But now the N/D method does not guarantee the asymptotic behavior $|g_\ell| \leq q^{-2\ell-1}$ required at $q^2 \to +\infty$ by unitarity. For each small segment of a cut gives a contribution $\sim q^{-2}$ at large q^2, and detailed cancellations would have to occur to give $\sim q^{-2\ell-1}$ for the whole amplitude. Of course, these cancellations will occur in a full solution of the Schrödinger equation, but that doesn't help us in the relativistic case. Thus it is time to turn to new methods -- the representations of Mandelstam and Regge, which avoid these difficulties by considering all partial waves together. The special role we have just noted for the lowest partial wave -- that it can be treated separately without violating asymptotic conditions -- will be explored further and related to the special role of particles with low spin in renormalizable field theory. Finally, the theory of Regge poles will suggest a more practical method for distinguishing between elementary and composite particles.

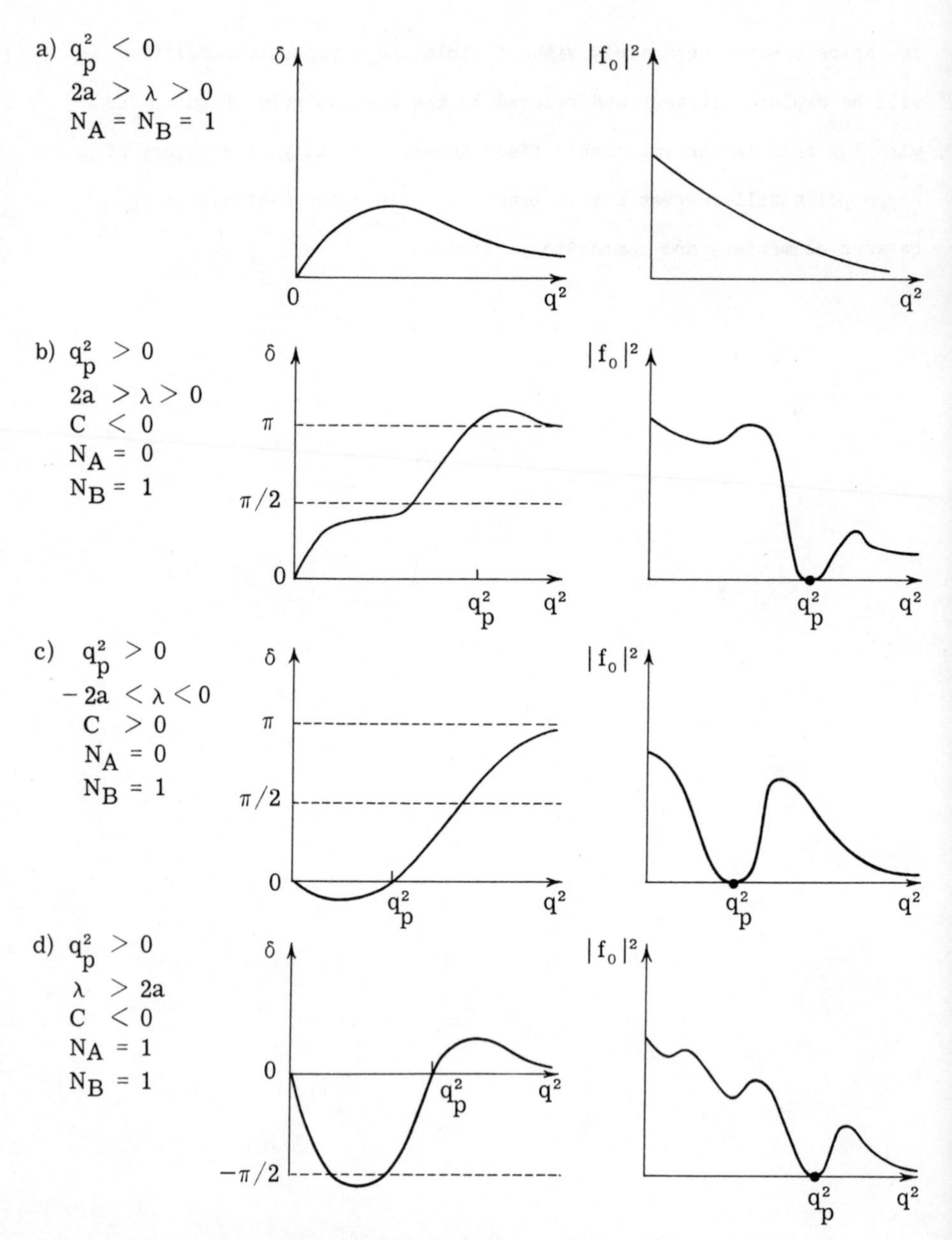

Figure 3-1 Some examples of the behavior of the S-wave phase shift and cross section as a function of energy, for the effective range formula with one CDD pole.

IV. THE MANDELSTAM REPRESENTATION FOR NON-RELATIVISTIC POTENTIAL SCATTERING

The source of much of our intuition, and most of the rigorous proofs for S-matrix theory, is non-relativistic potential scattering. Accordingly, we shall begin there and then present the relativistic theory as a natural generalization. Let us consider non-relativistic scattering by a superposition of Yukawa potentials:

$$V(r) = -\frac{1}{2M^2} \int_{t_o}^{\infty} dm^2 \, \rho_o(m^2) \, \frac{e^{-mr}}{r} \quad . \tag{4-1}$$

The scattering amplitude is

$$f(\Theta) = \frac{1}{q} \sum_{\ell=0}^{\infty} (2\ell+1) \, e^{i\delta_\ell} \sin \delta_\ell \, P_\ell(\cos\Theta) \quad . \tag{4-2}$$

The Fourier transform of the potential (Born approximation) gives $f(\Theta)$ a term

$$\frac{1}{\pi} \int_{t_o}^{\infty} dt' \, \frac{\rho_o(t')}{t' - t} \tag{4-3}$$

where the exchanged mass m^2 has been replaced by t' and $t = -2q^2(1-\cos\Theta)$ is the momentum transfer. Thus the potential introduces a cut along the real t axis at unphysical $t \left[\cos\Theta > 1\right]$.

We next inquire what consequences necessarily follow from the existence of a cut at $t_o \leq t < \infty$ together with unitarity. For the purposes of this argument, consider a more general discontinuity in t:

$$f(q^2,t) = \frac{1}{\pi} \int_{t_o}^{\infty} \frac{f_t\,(q^2,t')\,dt'}{t' - t} + R \tag{4-4}$$

where R is regular in t. The other condition we wish to combine with (4-4), unitarity, has previously been encountered in partial-wave amplitudes, where it could be written

$$\frac{f_\ell(q^2+i\epsilon) - f_\ell(q^2-i\epsilon)}{2i} = q\, f_\ell^*(q^2+i\epsilon)\, f_\ell(q^2+i\epsilon) \tag{4-5}$$

at $q^2 > 0$. We now need the sum over all partial waves, which is equivalent to

$$f_{q^2}(q^2, \cos\Theta) \equiv \frac{f(q^2+i\epsilon, \cos\Theta) - f(q^2-i\epsilon, \cos\Theta)}{2i}$$

$$= \frac{q}{4\pi} \int d\Omega'\, f^*(q^2+i\epsilon, \cos\Theta')\, f(q^2+i\epsilon, \cos\Theta) \tag{4-6}$$

at $q^2 > 0$, $-1 \leq \cos\Theta \leq 1$. The angle Θ connects initial and final directions and satisfies the familiar condition

$$\cos\Theta = \cos\Theta\cos\Theta' + \cos\phi'\sin\Theta\sin\Theta' \quad . \tag{4-7}$$

Now substitute the representation (4-4) into (4-6):

$$f_{q^2}(\cos\Theta) = \frac{q}{4\pi} \int d\Omega' \left[\frac{1}{\pi} \int_{t_o}^{\infty} \frac{dt'\, f_t(t')}{t' + 2q^2\,(1 - \cos\Theta')} + R\right]$$

$$\left[\frac{1}{\pi} \int_{t_o}^{\infty} \frac{dt''\, f_t(t'')}{t'' + 2q^2\,(1 - \cos\Theta)} + R\right] \tag{4-8}$$

and continue $\cos\theta$ out of the physical region, holding $q^2 > 0$ fixed. Initially, the discontinuity f_{q^2} remains real as it was in the physical region. But at sufficiently large $\cos\theta$, $2q^2 (1 - \cos\theta)$ becomes less than $-t_o$; f_{q^2} develops a cut and becomes complex. In his original paper, Mandelstam[21)] performed the integration over $d\Omega'$ and identified the cut in f_{q^2} as*

$$f_{q^2} = \frac{1}{\pi} \int^{\infty} f_{q^2,t} (q^2,t') \frac{dt'}{t' - t} \quad , \tag{4-9}$$

$$f_{q^2,t} (q^2,t) = \frac{1}{2\pi q} \int_{t_o}^{K=0} \int_{t_o} \frac{dt'\, dt''\, f_t^*(q^2,t')\, f_t(q^2,t'')}{K^{1/2}(q^2, t, t', t'')} \quad , \tag{4-10}$$

$$K^{1/2} = \left[t^2 + t'^2 + t''^2 - 2\,(tt' + t't'' + t''t) - \frac{t\, t'\, t''}{q^2}\right]^{1/2} \quad , \tag{4-11}$$

subject to the condition

$$t^{1/2} \geq t'^{1/2} + t''^{1/2} \quad . \tag{4-12}$$

The region of integration in (4-10) is finite (Fig. 4-1). The lower limit of integration in (4-9) lies at the junction of $K = 0$ with $t' = t'' = t_o$, where of the two roots of t yielded by $K = 0$, (4-12) instructs us to take the upper one. Equation (4-12) also has the important consequence that the behavior at large t is built up by iteration of behavior at smaller t.

---

*An average student can derive Eqs. (4-9) to (4-12) from (4-8) in about two days.

To see the relation of this buildup to the Born expansion of the potential, start with the potential term,

$$f_t^{(1)}(q^2,t) = \rho_o(t) \qquad t \geq t_o \quad . \tag{4-13}$$

According to (4-10), one finds the double spectral function

$$f^{(2)}_{q^2,t} = \frac{1}{2\pi q} \int_{t_o} \int_{t_o}^{K=0} dt'\, dt'' \, \frac{\rho_o(t')\, \rho_o(t'')}{K^{1/2}} \tag{4-14}$$

with boundary as indicated in Fig. 4-2. Now work back towards the complete amplitude. The single discontinuity f_{q^2} is given by (4-9). In the physical region, f_{q^2} is real and extends from $q^2 = 0$ to ∞, so the complete amplitude consists of the Cauchy integral

$$\frac{1}{\pi} \int_0^{\infty} \frac{dq'^2 \, f_{q^2}(q'^2, \cos \Theta)}{q'^2 - q^2} \tag{4-15}$$

plus terms regular in q^2. At this stage, then, the amplitude is (4-15) plus the Born term, or

$$\sum_{n=1}^{2} f^{(n)}(q^2,t) = \frac{1}{\pi} \int_0^{\infty} \frac{dt' \, \rho_o(t')}{t' - t} + \frac{1}{\pi^2} \int_0^{\infty} \frac{dq'^2}{q'^2 - q^2}$$

$$\times \int^{\infty} dt' \, \frac{f^{(2)}_{q^2,t}(q'^2, t')}{t' - t} \quad . \tag{4-16}$$

Since the potential acts twice in the second term, this term must have some connection with second-order Born approximation; in fact, Blankenbecler et al.[22] have shown that the second term is precisely second-order Born approximation. The interpretation of the cut at $t > 4\, t_o$ (Fig. 4-2) is that the potential introduces an exchange of objects with mass $\sqrt{t} \geq \sqrt{t_o}$ and that in second order the exchange occurs twice for a total exchanged mass of $\sqrt{t} \geq 2\sqrt{t_o}$.

Next we can find $f^{(3)}$ from

$$f^{(3)}_{q^2,t}\,(q^2,t) = \frac{1}{2\pi q} \int \int^{K=0} \frac{dt'\,dt''}{K^{1/2}} \left[f_t^{*(1)}(q^2,t')\, f_t^{(2)}(q^2,t'') + \text{C.C.} \right] \qquad (4\text{-}17)$$

and so forth. The nth iteration gives $f^{(n)}_{q^2,t}$ with a curved boundary at $t \geq n^2\, t_o$ in agreement with the interpretation of multiple exchange just given. After n iterations, the single and double spectral function f_t and $f_{q^2,t}$ are known exactly out to $t = (n + 1)^2\, t_o$ and partially at larger t. Thus f_t and $f_{q^2,t}$ can be calculated from the potential at any t and q^2 by a finite number of iterations.

For practice, the reader may iterate the simple Yukawa potential

$$\rho_o(t) = \pi\, \lambda\, \delta\,(t - t_o) \quad . \qquad (4\text{-}18)$$

One finds

$$f_t^{(2)}(q^2,t) = \frac{\pi\, \lambda^2}{2q\left[t^2 - 4\, t\, t_o - \frac{t\, t_o^2}{q^2} \right]^{1/2}} \quad . \qquad (4\text{-}19)$$

Here the boundary of the double spectral function is at

$$t = 4\, t_o + t_o^2/q^2 \tag{4-20}$$

as would be expected from the general boundary condition $K(q^2, t, t_o, t_o) = 0$. The explicit integrations cannot be carried out in higher orders, but the boundaries can still be located exactly from the vanishing of K.

The cuts we have located thus far, and the explicit prescriptions for calculating the discontinuity across them, are necessary consequences of unitarity and a superposition of Yukawa potentials. The analysis of Blankenbecler *et al.*,[22] and work by Regge,[23-25] established that these necessary discontinuities *completely determine the scattering amplitude*. When there are no bound states or resonances, the amplitude is

$$f(q^2,t) = \frac{1}{\pi}\int_{t_o}^{\infty} \frac{dt'\ \rho_o(t')}{t' - t} + \frac{1}{\pi^2}\int_{o}^{\infty} \frac{dq'^2}{q'^2 - q^2}\int \frac{dt'}{t'-t}\, f_{q^2,t}(q'^2,t')$$

$$= \frac{1}{\pi}\int_{t_o}^{\infty} dt'\ \frac{f_t(q^2,t')}{t' - t} \quad . \tag{4-21}$$

In the presence of bound states or resonances, a modified representation is required but f_t and $f_{q^2,t}$ still completely determine the amplitude. Bound states, resonances, and the related question of asymptotic behavior will be discussed later when we come to Regge poles.

The Mandelstam prescription we have just given for calculating the complete amplitude by dispersion relations provides an alternative method to the Schrödinger equation. This method is less familiar than the Schrödinger equation and seems to be valid only for a superposition of Yukawa potentials. But it generalizes in a natural way to relativistic problems where the Schrödinger equation breaks down. The situation seems analogous to classical mechanics, where certain special formulations provided the most natural bridge to wave mechanics.

Now let us try to become a little more familiar with the properties of the Mandelstam equation for non-relativistic scattering. One of the surprising features at first sight is the curved boundary of the double spectral function. To see the reason for this, consider the partial-wave amplitude

$$f_\ell = e^{i\delta_\ell} \frac{\sin \delta_\ell}{q} \tag{4-22}$$

near threshold where $\delta_\ell \sim q^{2\ell+1}$:

$$\text{Re } f_\ell \sim q^{2\ell} \quad , \tag{4-23}$$

$$\text{Im } f_\ell \sim q^{4\ell+1} \quad . \tag{4-24}$$

The partial wave is obtained by projection from f:

$$f_\ell = \frac{1}{2} \int_{-1}^{1} d \cos\Theta \, P_\ell(\cos\Theta) \, f(q^2, \cos\Theta) \quad . \tag{4-25}$$

The threshold behavior of Re f follows easily from

$$f_\ell = \frac{1}{2} \int_{-1}^{1} d\cos\theta \, P_\ell(\cos\theta) \, \frac{1}{\pi} \int_{t_o}^{\infty} \frac{f_t(t', q^2)}{t' - t} \quad , \tag{4-26}$$

for expanding the explicit $\cos\theta$ dependence

$$\frac{1}{t'-t} = \frac{1}{t' + 2q^2 (1 - \cos\theta)} = \frac{1}{t'+2q^2} \left[1 + \frac{2q^2 \cos\theta}{t' + 2q^2} + \ldots \right] \quad , \tag{4-27}$$

one naturally finds an additional power of q^2 associated with each additional power of $\cos\theta$. The threshold behavior of $\operatorname{Im} f_\ell$ is obtained from

$$\operatorname{Im} f_\ell = \frac{1}{2} \int_{-1}^{1} d\cos\theta \, P_\ell(\cos\theta) \, f_{q^2}(q^2, t)$$

$$= \frac{1}{2} \int_{-1}^{1} d\cos\theta \, P_\ell(\cos\theta) \, \frac{1}{\pi} \int^{\infty} \frac{f_{q^2,t}(q^2, t') \, dt'}{t' + 2q^2 (1 - \cos\theta)} \quad . \tag{4-28}$$

If the threshold of integration were at $t' = t_o$, we would again find $\operatorname{Im} f_\ell$ increasing by q^2 each time ℓ increases by one. But, in fact, the boundary is curved and behaves, according to (4-20), like $t' \sim t_o^2/q^2$ at small q^2. Thus at small q^2 we have

$$f_{q^2} \simeq \frac{1}{\pi} \int_{t_o^2/q^2} \frac{f_{q^2,t}(q^2,t')\ (q^2\,dt')}{q^2\,t' + 2q^4\,(1 - \cos\theta)}$$

$$\simeq \frac{1}{\pi} \int_{t_o^2}^{\infty} \frac{f_{q^2,t}(q^2,\ x/q^2)\ dx}{x + 2q^4\ (1 - \cos\theta)} \tag{4-29}$$

which explains how a factor q^4 becomes associated with each additional power of $\cos\theta$. Of course, it is not surprising that the curved boundary is consistent with unitarity at threshold, because the curved boundary was derived with the help of unitarity.

Another limiting case which is easy to discuss is the high energy limit $q^2 \to \infty$ at fixed t. The potential term is constant in this limit. Each higher order term vanishes when $q^2 \to \infty$, because of the factor q^{-1} in (4-10). Thus the amplitude approaches Born approximation in the high-energy limit, a familiar property of non-relativistic scattering from Yukawa potentials. As a consequence, the integration

$$f_t^{(n)}(q^2,t) = \frac{1}{\pi} \int^{\infty} dq'^2\ \frac{f_{q^2,t}^{(n)}\ (q'^2,t)}{q'^2 - q^2} \tag{4-30}$$

which is required after each iteration of $f_{q^2,t}^{(n)}$ in order to compute the input for the next iteration (see Eq. (4-10)), converges in each order of the Born expansion. The sensible behavior of the Mandelstam representation in both low and high q^2 limits is in sharp contrast to the difficulties encountered in these limits with the N/D method.

The asymptotic behavior in t, and the convergence or non-convergence of the Born series for f (the integral over f_t) are more subtle matters which will be discussed later in connection with Regge poles.

Problem: Assume that the complete solution has the property

$$f_t \sim \beta(q^2)\, t^{\alpha(q^2)} \tag{4-31}$$

as $t \to \infty$ at fixed q^2, and assume that β has a cut running from $q^2 = 0$ to ∞ (these properties actually follow from Regge's work). The discontinuity in q^2, $f_{q^2,t}$, can be read off directly from (4-31) and grows at the rate: $t^{\mathrm{Re}(\alpha)}$ as $t \to \infty$.

In a consistent solution, $f_{q^2,t}$ as calculated from (4-10) with input $f_t \sim \beta t^\alpha$, must also grow at the rate $t^{\mathrm{Re}(\alpha)}$. Show that this is so only if $\alpha(q^2)$ is complex at the positive q^2 where (4-10) is applied.

As a final application, we shall use the Mandelstam representation to locate the left cut of the partial-wave amplitudes. From (4-26), we have

$$f_\ell(q^2) = \frac{1}{2} \int_{-1}^{1} d\cos\theta\, P_\ell(\cos\theta)\, \frac{1}{\pi} \int_{t_0}^{\infty} \frac{f_t(t',q^2)\, dt'}{t' + 2q^2\,(1 - \cos\theta)} \; . \tag{4-32}$$

At negative q^2, the discontinuity function

$$f_t(t',q^2) = \rho_0(t') + \frac{1}{\pi} \int^{\infty} \frac{dq'^2}{q'^2 - q^2} f_{q^2,t}(t', q'^2) \qquad (4\text{-}33)$$

is real because the boundary of the double spectral function lies at $q^2 \geq 0$. The only way a discontinuity can occur in f_ℓ is by vanishing of the denominator

$$t' + 2q^2 (1 - \cos\Theta) = 0 \qquad (4\text{-}34)$$

in the range of integration $t' \geq t_o$, $-1 \leq \cos\Theta \leq 1$. This happens at

$$q^2 = -\frac{t_o}{4} \quad , \qquad (4\text{-}35)$$

signaling the start of the left cut. The left cuts associated with the higher Born terms $t' \geq n^2 t_o$ start at

$$q^2 = -\frac{n^2 t_o}{4} \quad . \qquad (4\text{-}36)$$

Of course, the right cut is also contained in the Mandelstam representation (4-28). Note that the left cut moves further and further away as the order of iteration increases. The association of high-order Born terms with exchange of large masses leads to the usual connection between short-range effects and far-away singularities in q^2.

If the double spectral function is known, the left cut of f_ℓ can be obtained from the projection (4-32) and the N/D method can be used to calculate the right cut. As we have seen, this leads to difficulties at threshold or large q^2 for $\ell > 0$, and it would certainly be more straightforward to project the entire partial-wave amplitude out of the Mandelstam representation, if the double spectral function were completely known. But if $f_{q^2,t}$ is known only in low orders so that only the nearby left cut is determined, the N/D method does ensure unitarity and can provide generalized effective range formulae at energies sufficiently low that the distance to the known part of the left cut is a small fraction of the distance to the unknown part.

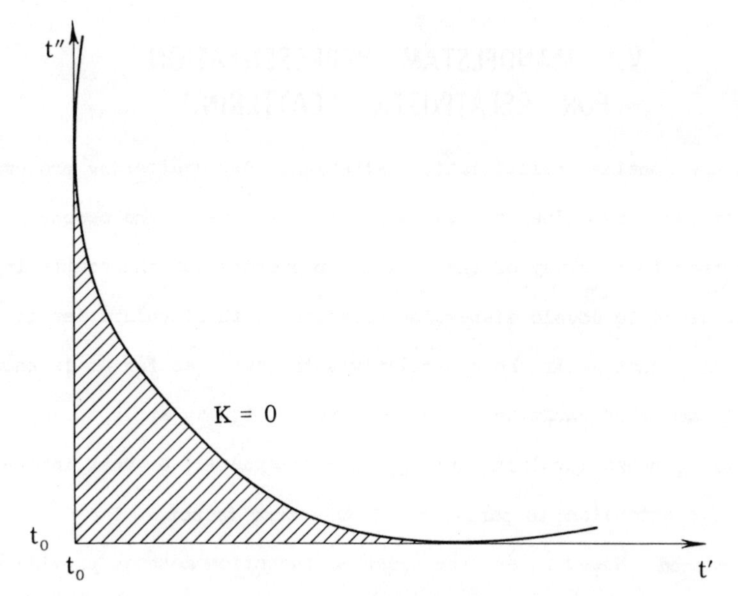

Figure 4-1 The region of integration used in determining the double spectral function (Eq. 4-10).

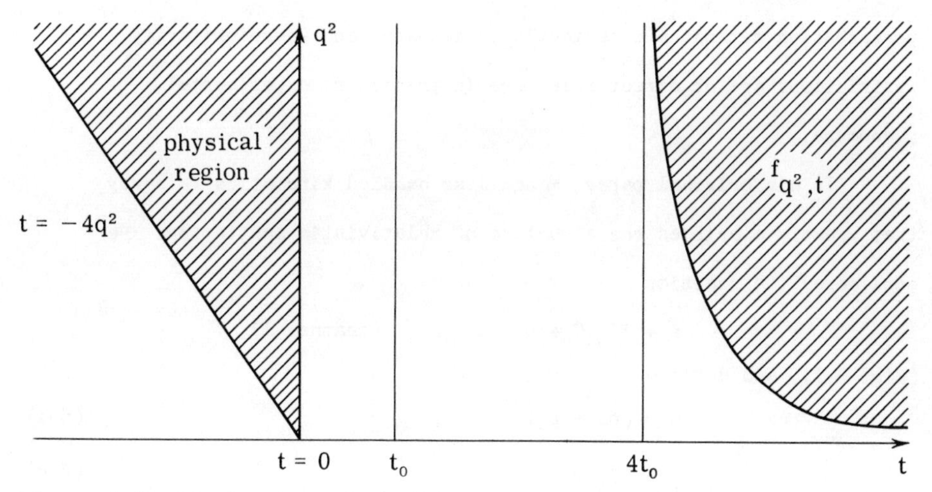

Figure 4-2 The location of the physical region and the boundary of the double spectral function.

V. MANDELSTAM REPRESENTATION FOR RELATIVISTIC SCATTERING

We now consider relativistic scattering. Any scattering process involves at least two kinematic variables such as energy and momentum transfer; therefore, study of the analytic properties of the scattering amplitudes leads to double dispersion relations with singularities in two variables, just as in the non-relativistic case. As far as is known, the Mandelstam representation, or extensions of it, may apply to any relativistic process involving strong, electromagnetic, or weak interactions. The extension to particles of mass zero is not fully understood, however, and the older perturbation methods provide a very accurate description of a wide class of experiments on purely electromagnetic or weak interaction phenomena. Thus we shall confine our discussion to the strong interactions, which is the place where perturbation methods are obviously inadequate, and where unitarity restrictions are of direct relevance in predicting experimental phenomena.

In his original paper, Mandelstam handled kinematics in a way that greatly clarifies the structure of relativistic scattering. He considered the reaction

$$A + B \rightarrow C + D \qquad \text{(channel I)}$$

(Fig. 5-1), and defined:

$$s = (p_1 + p_2)^2 \quad , \tag{5-1}$$

$$t = (p_1 - p_3)^2 \quad , \tag{5-2}$$

$$u = (p_1 - p_4)^2 \quad . \tag{5-3}$$

Two-body scattering depends on two variables (e.g., energy and angle), so the three variables have a constraint which can be deduced from energy-momentum conservation:

$$s + t + u = \sum_{i=1}^{4} m_i^2 \quad . \tag{5-4}$$

In channel I, s has the significance of center-of-mass energy squared, t represents momentum transfer from A to C, and u represents momentum transfer from A to D. If the masses are equal (as we assume henceforth) and "forward scattering" is defined as C emerging in the same direction as A, we have in channel I

$$s = 4\,(q_s^2 + m^2) \quad , \tag{5-5}$$

$$t = -\,2q_s^2\,(1 - \cos\theta_s) \quad , \tag{5-6}$$

$$u = -\,2q_s^2\,(1 + \cos\theta_s) \quad . \tag{5-7}$$

where q_s is the center-of-mass momentum and θ_s the center-of-mass angle.

The unique properties of relativistic scattering become manifest when we recognize the existence of two more reactions:

$$A + \bar{C} \rightarrow D + \bar{B} \qquad \text{(channel II)} \quad ,$$

$$A + \bar{D} \rightarrow C + \bar{B} \qquad \text{(channel III)} \quad .$$

The physical region of channel II, for example, is reached by continuing p_3 from the region $E_3 \geq m$ where it represents a particle, through the unphysical region $-m < E_3 < m$, to $E_3 \leq -m$ where it represents an antiparticle. If we give the antiparticles positive energies by defining $p_{\bar{C}} = - p_3$ and $p_{\bar{B}} = - p_2$, the kinetic variables take the form

$$s = (p_1 - p_{\bar{B}})^2 \quad , \tag{5-8}$$

$$t = (p_1 + p_{\bar{C}})^2 \quad , \tag{5-9}$$

$$u = (p_1 - p_4)^2 \quad . \tag{5-10}$$

For the equal mass case in channel II, evaluated in the center-of-mass,

$$t = 4\ (q_t^{\ 2} + m^2) \tag{5-11}$$

is the energy variable while

$$s = - 2q_t^{\ 2}\ (1 + \cos \Theta_t) \quad , \tag{5-12}$$

$$u = - 2q_t^{\ 2}\ (1 - \cos \Theta_t) \tag{5-13}$$

are momentum transfer variables (we have defined Θ_t as the angle between $\vec{p}_1$ and $\vec{p}_4$). In channel III, u becomes the energy variable. Each kinematic variable plays a double role as an energy variable in one channel and a momentum transfer variable in two other channels. A channel is often named by its energy variable; thus channel I is the "s-channel".

The physical regions can be represented on a two-dimensional diagram (Fig. 5-2). There are two dimensions because physical s, t, and u are real variables connected by the constraint (5-4). In each physical region, the energy variable exceeds $4m^2$ and the momentum transfers are negative; for example in channel I, $s \geq 4m^2$, $t \leq 0$, $u \leq 0$. Figure 5-2 emphasizes the equivalent roles played by all three channels. Evidently, the physical regions are plane segments separated by, and immersed in, an unphysical sea (only the part of the unphysical region where s, t, and u are real appears in Fig. 5-2).

Now the non-relativistic scattering amplitude f has to be replaced by one or more invariant amplitudes in the relativistic case. The number of these depends on the spins and isotopic spins of A, B, C, and D. For simplicity, consider particles with spin zero and isotopic spin zero; then there is only one amplitude which can conveniently be defined in channel I as

$$A(s,t,u) = \frac{\sqrt{q_s^2+m^2}}{q_s} \sum_{\ell=0}^{\infty} (2\ell+1) \frac{(e^{2i\delta_\ell} - 1)}{2i} P_\ell(\cos\theta) \quad . \qquad (5\text{-}14)$$

The crucial crossing relations state that the same invariant function A governs scattering in channels II and III. This means we can write

$$A(s,t,u) = \frac{\sqrt{q_t^2+m^2}}{q_t} \sum_{\ell=0}^{\infty} (2\ell+1) \frac{(e^{2i\delta_\ell} - 1)}{2i} P_\ell(\cos\theta_t) \quad , \qquad (5\text{-}15)$$

and a similar representation for channel III. These relations were first suggested by substitutions (e.g., $p_3 \to -p_3$, $p_2 \to -p_2$ to pass from channel I to channel II) in perturbation theory. But the physical regions in Fig. 5-2 do not overlap, so the crossing relation is empty -- the function need not be the same -- unless an analytic continuation can be made from one physical region to another. The existence of such analytic continuations has been confirmed for many individual diagrams in perturbation theory, and no counter-examples have been found. However, a general proof on the basis of perturbation theory or axiomatic field theory does not exist at the present time. We shall <u>assume</u> the crossing relations.

A related but more specialized condition is <u>crossing symmetry</u>. It arises when the same reaction occurs in two channels.

<u>Example</u>: If $\bar{C} = B$, then $\bar{B} = C$ and the reactions of channels I and II are the same. The amplitude satisfies the condition:

$$A(s,t,u) = A(t,s,u) \tag{5-16}$$

which may also be viewed as the symmetry of the amplitude for channel III under interchange of two identical spin zero particles ($\cos\Theta_u \to -\cos\Theta_u$ when s and t are interchanged).

In the non-relativistic case we found that the unitarity relation $\mathrm{Im}\, f_\ell = q\, f_\ell^* f_\ell$ at real positive q^2 forced each partial wave to have a phase; the phase was δ_ℓ at $q^2 + i\epsilon$ and $-\delta_\ell$ at $q^2 - i\epsilon$. This caused a cut from $q^2 = 0$ to $q^2 = \infty$. The other cut, in t, was a special property of a superposition of Yukawa potentials, and the choice of this cut was quite arbitrary. If we liked we could also have added an "exchange potential" -- a cut in u.

In the relativistic case, unitarity again causes a cut from $q_s^2 = 0$ to $q_s^2 = \infty$, i.e., from $s = 4m^2$ to ∞. The crossing relations also force us to impose unitarity in the t and u channels, resulting in cuts at $4m^2 \leq t < \infty$ and $4m^2 \leq u < \infty$. In other words, all these cuts now have an equivalent physical basis. All are now subject to unitarity -- the arbitrariness of t and u cuts is greatly reduced in passing to the relativistic case.

While studying non-relativistic scattering, we deduced the consequences of a cut in t and unitarity in the s-channel. In completely analogous fashion, we can now deduce the consequences of cuts at real $t > 4m^2$ and $u > 4m^2$, and elastic unitarity in the s-channel. The only new features are a factor $\sqrt{q_s^2 + m^2}$ from relativistic kinematics, and exchange terms from the u cut, which could have been included already in the non-relativistic case. One finds double spectral functions

$$A_{st} = \frac{1}{\pi q_s \sqrt{s}} \int_{4m^2} \int_{4m^2}^{K=0} \left[\frac{dt' \, dt'' \, A_t^*(s,t') \, A_t(s,t'')}{K^{1/2} (q_s^2, t, t', t'')} + \frac{du' \, du'' \, A_u^*(s,u') \, A_u(s,u'')}{K^{1/2} (q_s^2, t, u', u'')} \right] \tag{5-17}$$

and a similar relation for A_{su} in which t is replaced by u and the bilinear combinations $A_t^* A_u$ and $A_u^* A_t$ appear. In other words, the cut in the "direct" momentum transfer variable t is the product of two direct terms plus the product of two exchange terms, while the cut in the "exchange" momentum transfer u is a product of a direct and an exchange term. The double spectral functions we have just located are indicated in Fig. 5-3.

The same arguments apply to the cuts at $u \geq 4m^2$ and $s \geq 4m^2$ together with unitarity in the t-channel, or the cuts at $s \geq 4m^2$ and $t \geq 4m^2$ together with unitarity in the u-channel. The new double spectral functions obtained in this way are also indicated in Fig. 5-3. The corresponding representation, ignoring subtraction terms for the moment, is

$$A(s,t,u) = \frac{1}{\pi^2} \int\int \frac{ds'\, dt'\, A_{st}(s',t')}{(s'-s)\,(t'-t)} + \frac{1}{\pi^2} \int\int \frac{ds'\, du'\, A_{su}(s',u')}{(s'-s)\,(u'-u)}$$

$$+ \frac{1}{\pi^2} \int\int \frac{dt'\, du'\, A_{tu}(t',u')}{(t'-t)\,(u'-u)} \quad . \tag{5-18}$$

The boundaries of the double spectral function are indicated in Fig. 5-3. In the s-channel, for example, there is one part of A_{st} with threshold at $s = 4m^2$ and another part with threshold at $s = 16m^2$. The significance of the two parts can easily be seen with the aid of Cutkosky diagrams. Cutkosky diagrams look like Feynman diagrams but are interpreted differently: each line is on the mass shell and the vertices connecting lines are general -- not restricted to a particular order of perturbation theory. We start with the existence of a unitarity cut in the t-channel (two-particle intermediate state on the mass shell with $t \geq 4m^2$, Fig. 5-4). We apply elastic unitarity, $A_s = \int A^+ A$, in the s-channel. This bilinear expression in A, connected by a two-particle intermediate state in the s-channel (Fig. 5-5a), has cuts at $s \geq (2m)^2$,

$t \geq (4m)^2$. So far, this is just what happened in the non-relativistic case. But now the unitarity cut at $s \geq 4m^2$ can be considered together with elastic unitarity in the t-channel, $A_t = \int A^+ A$. This bilinear expression gives a new diagram in which the roles of s and t are interchanged (Fig. 5-5b) to give thresholds $t = (2m)^2$, $s = (4m)^2$. The physical interpretation of the new diagram in the s-channel is: inelastic scattering with threshold at $s = (4m)^2$.

Up to this point we have applied elastic unitarity in each channel, which is entirely correct in the elastic regions $4m^2 \leq s < 16m^2$, $4m^2 \leq t < 16m^2$, $4m^2 \leq u < 16m^2$. All terms calculated thus far were elastic in at least one channel. Above inelastic thresholds, the unitarity condition of course involves contributions from inelastic intermediate states as well. This leads to new terms which are not elastic in any channel, such as Fig. 5-6. The new terms do not change the representation (5-18) (still ignoring subtractions); they merely give new contributions to the double spectral functions. Since the new contributions are inelastic in each channel, they do not enlarge the region covered by double spectral function; for example, the new contributions to A_{st} are bounded by $s \geq 16m^2$ and $t \geq 16m^2$.

The preceding discussion of boundaries has been appropriate for pion-pion scattering, where conservation of G parity prevents transitions from an even number of pions to an odd number. If we continue to assume equal masses but drop the conservation law, a pole (one-particle intermediate state) appears at $s = m^2$, etc., and the inelastic thresholds begin at $s = (3m)^2$, etc.

Exercise: Sketch the figure that replaces Fig. 5-2 when two of the masses differ, as in $\pi + N \to \pi + N$ (treated in Reference 21). Find the static limit ($m_N \to \infty$, m_π remains finite).

All of the cuts located thus far in the relativistic case are necessary consequences of unitarity. As in non-relativistic scattering, the question arises: are there more singularities and does unitarity determine all of them ("maximal analyticity")? First, let us consider the evidence on additional singularities. Investigation of this question is difficult in the relativistic case; we do not know the properties of the complete solution or even whether present theories have a consistent solution. The greatest progress has come through the development by Landau,[26] Bjorken,* and others of a general method for locating the singularities of Feynman diagrams. For many elastic scattering processes, such as $\pi + \pi \to \pi + \pi$, $\pi + N \to \pi + N$, and $N + N \to N + N$, they found in low orders of perturbation theory only Mandelstam cuts and single-particle poles. Eden, Landshoff, Polkinghorne, and Taylor went a long way towards verifying this for an arbitrary diagram, but were unable to give a general proof.[27] For the purposes of further discussion, we shall assume the Mandelstam representation is correct

*J. Bjorken, unpublished Stanford University preprint (1959).

for the processes mentioned above.* This allows us to cross from one physical region to another, so the crossing relations are included in the assumption.

In many other processes, further "anomalous" singularities are found (see, e.g., References 28 and 29). This is always the case for reactions involving more than two particles. Even in two-body reactions, anomalous singularities not included in the Mandelstam representation can occur. This happens, for example, if the wave function (speaking non-relativistically) of an external particle extends beyond the range of the forces. To be specific, consider $\Sigma + \Sigma \rightarrow \Sigma + \Sigma$. The two-pion exchange diagram (Fig. 5-7) has the usual branch point at $t = 4m_\pi^2$, corresponding to an interaction distance $R \sim \frac{1}{2} m_\pi$. But a Σ can undergo a virtual transition $\Sigma \rightarrow \Lambda + \pi \rightarrow \Sigma$ (whether or not Σ is a bound state of the $\Lambda\pi$ system) with a small energy denominator corresponding to a spatial extension exceeding $1/m_\pi$. Thus it is not surprising that Fig. 5-7 has an additional or "anomalous" threshold at $t < 4m_\pi^2$, to be interpreted in terms of the extra large interaction distance resulting from the large "size" of the Σ.

Although anomalous singularities require a more complicated representation than Mandelstam's, they grow continuously out of the Mandelstam singularities as the masses are varied (e.g., Reference 30), and thus there is reason to believe that they too follow from unitarity (see also Reference 31). With that, we leave the subject of

*There is a story about the student who wanted to know, "Can one prove the Mandelstam representation from field theory?" He went to Weisskopf who responded, "Field theory, what is field theory?" Then he sought out Wigner who said, "Mandelstam, who is Mandelstam?" Finally, our persistent student found his way to Chew, repeated the question, and heard, "Proof, what is proof?"

anomalous singularities and return to the simpler problems like $\pi + \pi \rightarrow \pi + \pi$, $\pi + N \rightarrow \pi + N$, and $N + N \rightarrow N + N$. Here the Mandelstam representation may hold and unitarity controls the discontinuities across all cuts. There remains, however, the possibility of CDD poles -- which are not determined by unitarity.

As an example of how CDD poles appear in perturbation theory, consider $\pi + \pi \rightarrow \pi + \pi$. The S-wave can be treated by the N/D method. An extra pole term $C/s-s_1$ can be added to the denominator function without violating unitarity. As a result, D also acquires a new zero at s_2. Multiplication of both N and D by $(s-s_1)/(s-s_2)$ transfers the poles and zero to N. The two arbitrary constants introduced by the CDD can be expressed in various equivalent ways -- for example, as the position and residue $C'/s-s_2$ of the new pole in the amplitude. Now if C' and s_2 approach infinity in such a way that $C'/s-s_2$ remains finite, the one remaining arbitrary constant can be expressed as the value of the S-wave at some definite energy s_o. Equivalently, the entire amplitude contains one arbitrary constant at s_o and some definite t_o and u_o. This in turn is equivalent to the arbitrariness introduced in perturbation theory by a $\lambda \phi_\pi^4$ term in the Lagrangian. The renormalized coupling constant λ defines the amplitude at some definite s_o, t_o, and u_o.

Let us represent the $\lambda \phi_\pi^4$ term in the S-matrix by the diagram in Fig. 5-8a. This diagram, together with unitarity, necessarily leads to the familiar "chain diagrams" (Fig. 5-8b,c). Evidently, the "chain diagrams" are represented by a cut in only one variable (s in Fig. 5-8b, for example). So the double spectral function terms of Eq. (5-18) cannot give "chain diagrams", just as they cannot ensure that the S-matrix has the proper value at the point where it is defined by the renormalized coupling constant.

Further difficulties appear when we try to iterate the λ term. In lowest order we have (ignoring numerical coefficients) $A = \lambda$, which is an S-wave for each reaction. Iterating in the t-channel, we find:

$$A_t = \frac{q_t}{\sqrt{q_t^2+m^2}} A^* A = \frac{q_t \lambda^2}{\sqrt{q_t^2+m^2}} \xrightarrow[t \to \infty]{} \lambda^2 \quad . \tag{5-19}$$

This in turn can be substituted into Eq. (5-17) for the double spectral function, with the result

$$A_{st} \propto \lambda^4 \log t \quad \text{as} \quad t \to \infty \quad . \tag{5-20}$$

From the point of view of diagrams, we have computed the discontinuity for Fig. 5-5a. Now the integral

$$\frac{1}{\pi^2} \int \int \frac{ds'\, dt'\, A_{st}(s',t')}{(s'-s)\,(t'-t)} \tag{5-21}$$

fails to converge at large t'. So we are forced to make subtractions in t. In similar fashion one finds that subtractions in s and u are necessary. A double integral such as (5-21) requires subtractions in both s and t, while a single integral such as

$$\frac{1}{\pi} \int \frac{dt' A_t(t')}{t' - t} \tag{5-22}$$

requires one subtraction according to (5-19). The complete subtracted representation which replaces (5-18) is

$$\begin{aligned} A(s,t,u) = A(s_o,t_o,u_o) &+ \frac{(s-s_o)}{\pi} \int_{4m^2}^{\infty} \frac{\rho_1(s')\, ds'}{(s'-s)(s'-s_o)} \\ &+ \frac{(t-t_o)}{\pi} \int_{4m^2}^{\infty} \frac{\rho_2(t')\, dt'}{(t'-t)(t'-t_o)} + \frac{(u-u_o)}{\pi} \int_{4m^2}^{\infty} \frac{\rho_3(u')\, du'}{(u'-u)(u'-u_o)} \\ &+ \frac{(s-s_o)(t-t_o)}{\pi^2} \int\int \frac{A_{st}(s',t')\, ds'\, dt'}{(s'-s)(s'-s_o)(t'-t)(t'-t_o)} \\ &+ \frac{(s-s_o)(u-u_o)}{\pi^2} \int\int \frac{A_{su}(s',u')\, ds'\, du'}{(s'-s)(s'-s_o)(u'-u)(u'-u_o)} \\ &+ \frac{(t-t_o)(u-u_o)}{\pi^2} \int\int \frac{A_{tu}(t',u')\, dt'\, du'}{(t'-t)(t'-t_o)(u'-u)(u'-u_o)} \quad . \end{aligned} \tag{5-23}$$

The subtracted representation expresses perturbation theory better than (5-18) in three respects:

(a) Each integral now converges for each order of perturbation theory (note that all the subtractions were necessary).

(b) The single integral terms are now available to represent "chain diagrams".

(c) The subtractions have all been made to the point $s = s_o$, $t = t_o$, $u = u_o$, permitting us to define A at that point in terms of an arbitrary renormalized constant.

The single integral terms have a special relation to the partial wave in which the CDD pole was introduced. Consider the s-channel and Eq. (5-23). The three discontinuities at $s > 4m^2$ are ρ_1, A_{st}, A_{su}. Of these, ρ_1 contributes only to the S-wave, and the double spectral functions determine the right cuts of all higher partial waves. What is special about the S-wave is that it is not completely determined by the left cut plus unitarity, but also depends on the angle-independent CDD term $A(s_o, t_o, u_o)$, which leads to ρ_1.

The nucleon and pion poles in $\pi + N \rightarrow \pi + N$ and $N + N \rightarrow N + N$ can also be introduced as CDD poles, which lead to single integral terms in the $J = 1/2$, $T = 1/2$, and $J = 0$, $T = 1$ states respectively. These actually appear in perturbation theory because the $\pi N\bar{N}$ coupling term of the usual Lagrangian formulation introduces the arbitrary parameters g, m_π, and M_N into these states. In particular, diagrams such as Fig. 5-9 which can be cut in only one variable are represented by single integrals and poles, just as the $\pi\pi$ chain diagrams were represented by single integrals and the subtraction constant.

Although the CDD poles discussed here were all equivalent to coupling constants and stable particles of the old Lagrangian approach, it should be remembered that CDD poles can equally well introduce unstable particles.

The Mandelstam representation (5-23) allows an easy derivation of the older one-dimensional dispersion relations, which it is convenient to give here. The discontinuities of (5-23) in s, t, and u are:

$$A_s = \rho_1(s) + \frac{(t-t_o)}{\pi} \int \frac{A_{st}(s',t')\, dt'}{(t'-t)(t'-t_o)} + \frac{(u-u_o)}{\pi} \int \frac{A_{su}(s',u')\, du'}{(u'-u)(u'-u_o)} , \qquad (5\text{-}24)$$

$$A_t = \rho_2(t) + \frac{(s-s_o)}{\pi} \int \frac{A_{st}(s',t')\, ds'}{(s'-s)(s'-s_o)} + \frac{(u-u_o)}{\pi} \int \frac{A_{tu}(t',u')\, du'}{(u'-u)(u'-u_o)} , \qquad (5\text{-}25)$$

$$A_u = \rho_3(u) + \frac{(s-s_o)}{\pi} \int \frac{A_{su}(s',u')\, ds'}{(s'-s)(s'-s_o)} + \frac{(t-t_o)}{\pi} \int \frac{A_{tu}(t',u')\, dt'}{(t'-t)(t'-t_o)} . \qquad (5\text{-}26)$$

The Mandelstam representation can be rewritten in terms of these discontinuities as

$$\begin{aligned} A(s,t,u) = A(s_o,t_o,u_o) &+ \frac{(t-t_o)}{\pi} \int \frac{dt'\, \rho_2(t')}{(t'-t)(t'-t_o)} \\ &+ \frac{(s-s_o)}{\pi} \int \frac{ds'\, A_s(s',\, t,\, \Sigma\, m^2 - s' - t)}{(s'-s)\,(s'-s_o)} \\ &+ \frac{(u-u_o)}{\pi} \int \frac{du'\, A_u(\Sigma\, m^2 - t - u',\, t,\, u')}{(u'-u)\,(u'-u_o)} , \end{aligned} \qquad (5\text{-}27)$$

or similarly as a function of ρ_1, A_t, and A_u, or ρ_3, A_s, and A_t.

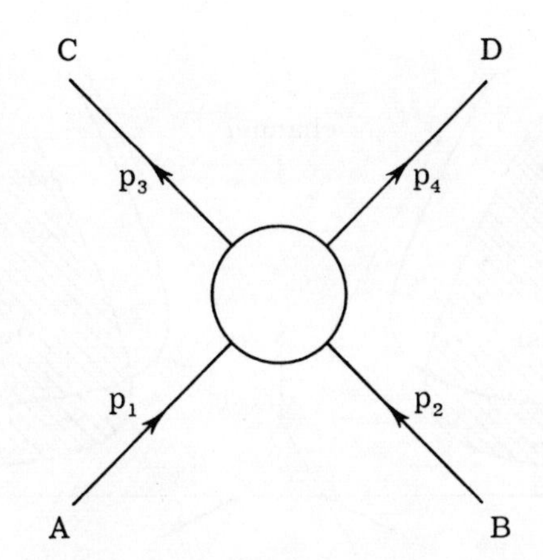

Figure 5-1 Diagram for the reaction A + B → C + D.

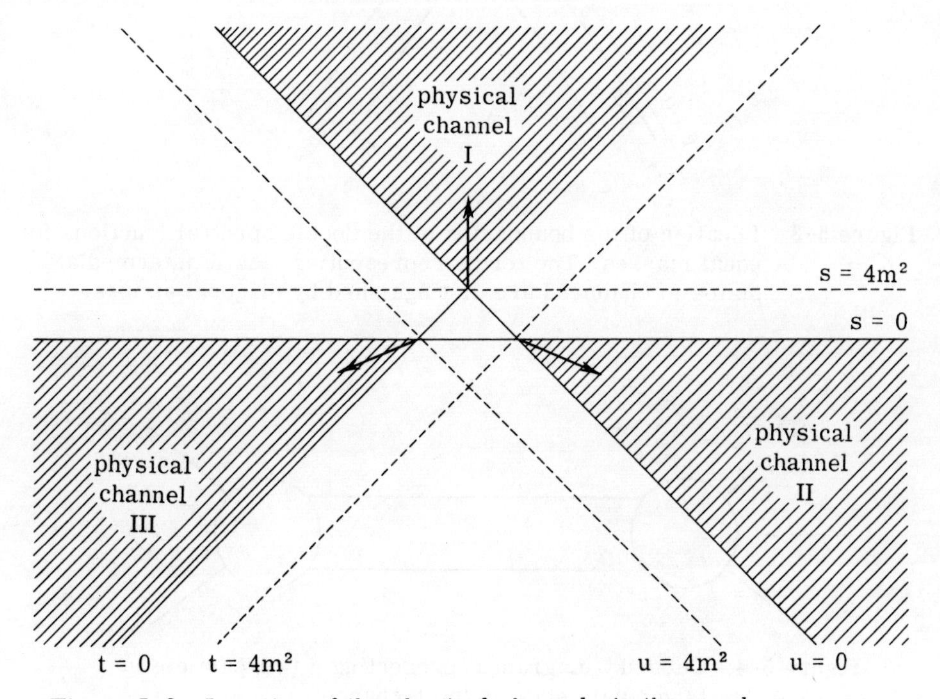

Figure 5-2 Location of the physical channels in the equal mass case.

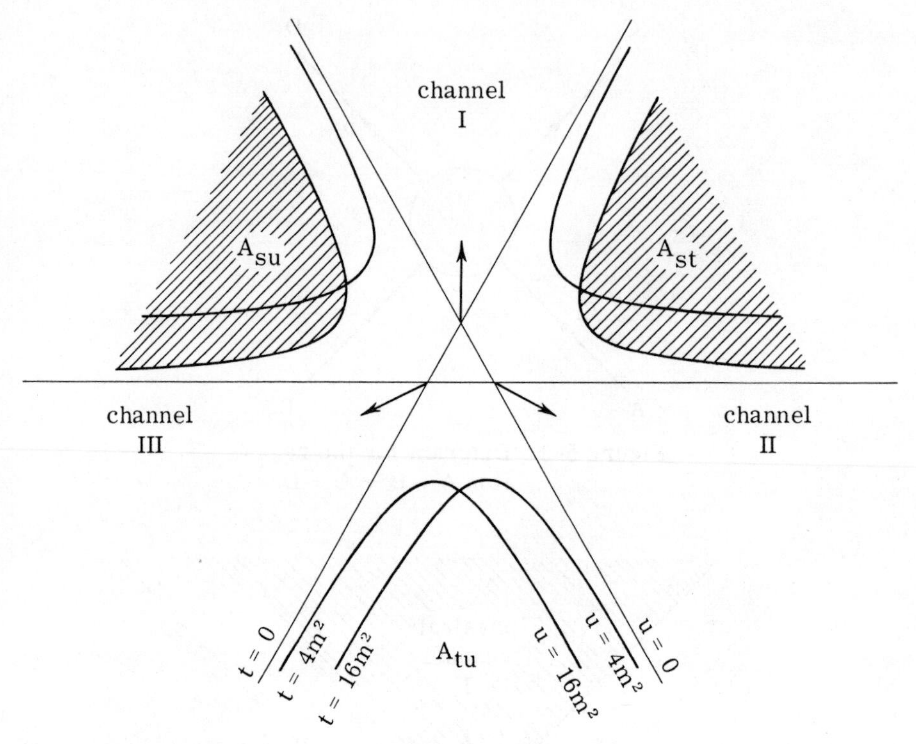

Figure 5-3 Location of the boundaries of the double spectral functions for equal masses. The terms representing elastic intermediate states in channel I are distinguished by diagonal stripes.

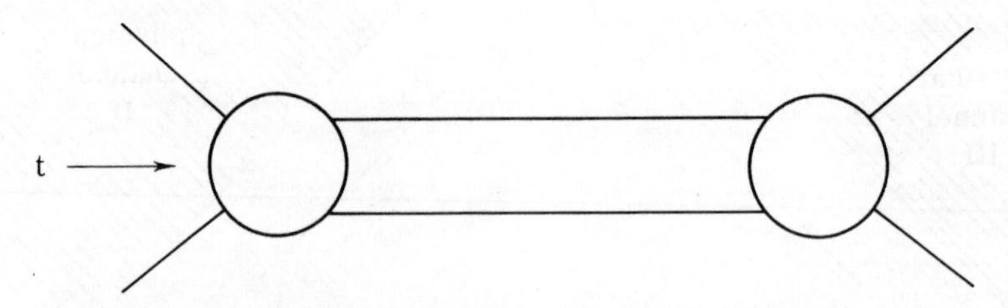

Figure 5-4 Cutkosky diagram representing a two-particle intermediate state in the t-channel.

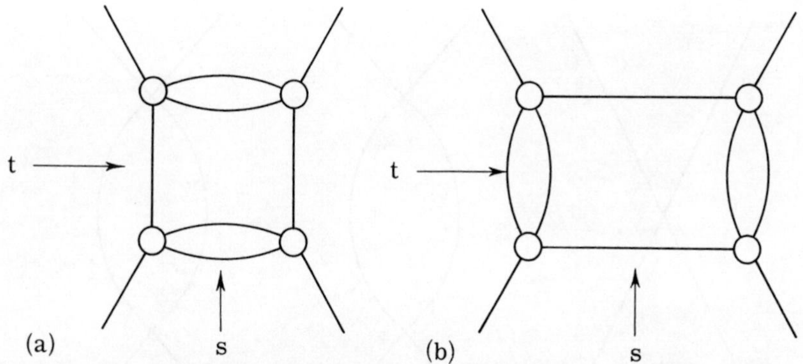

Figure 5-5 Cutkosky diagrams representing a two-particle intermediate state in one channel and a four-particle intermediate state in a crossed channel.

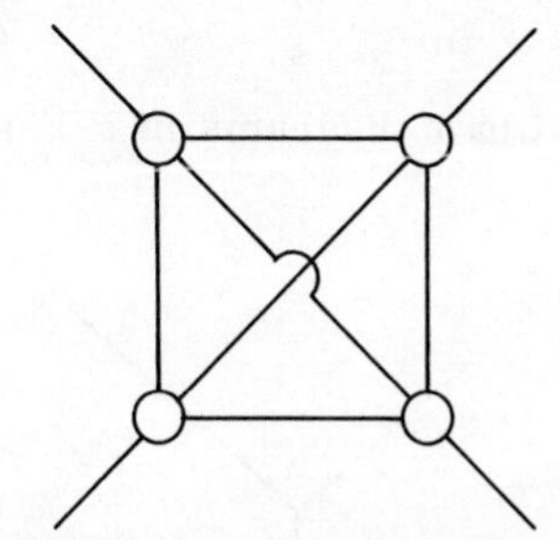

Figure 5-6 Cutkosky diagram which has a four-particle intermediate state in each channel.

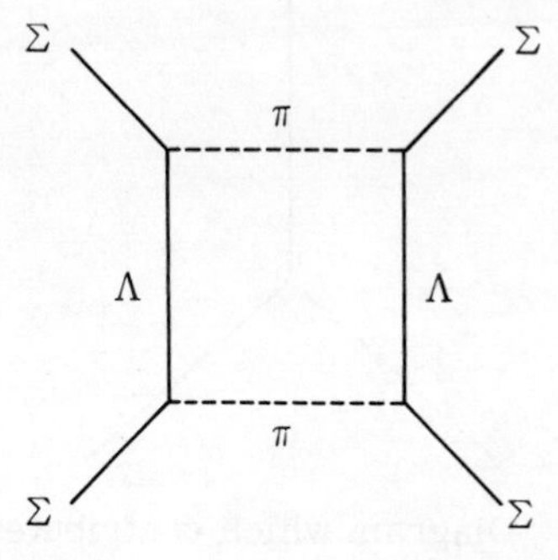

Figure 5-7 Example of a diagram with anomalous singularities.

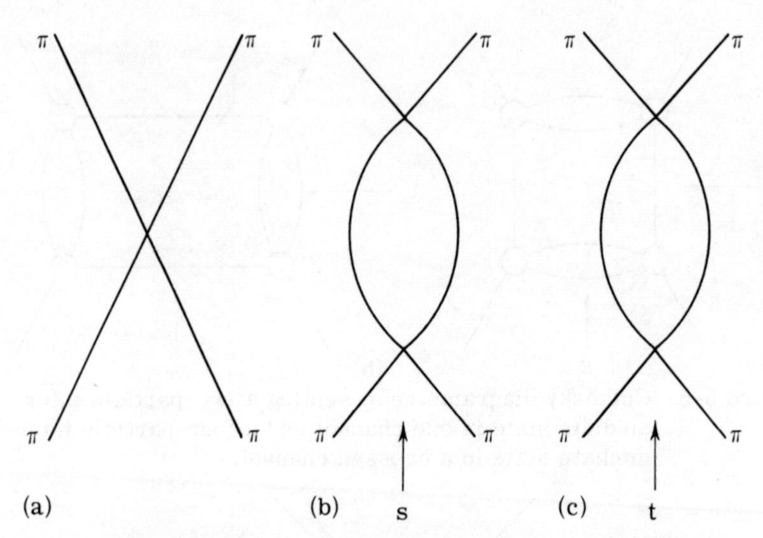

Figure 5-8 Chain diagrams in π-π scattering.

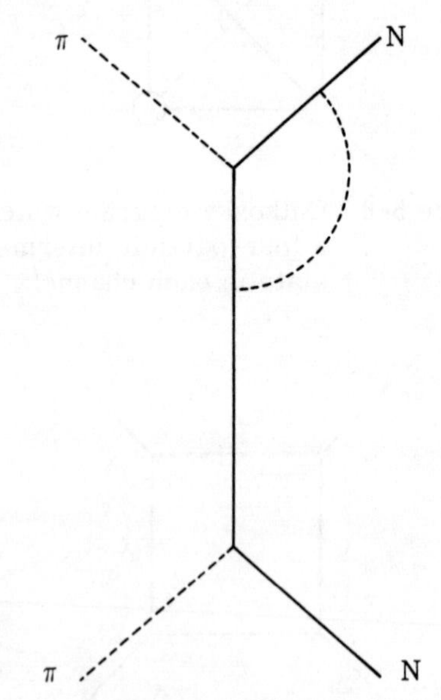

Figure 5-9 Diagram which contributes to the single integral in π-N scattering.

VI. THE GENERALIZED POTENTIAL

Much of our discussion about the Mandelstam representation has concerned the location of singularities. A further question of great dynamical importance is: how does one determine the discontinuities across singularities?

We have already seen how discontinuities associated with elastic intermediate states can be determined by elastic unitarity. Discontinuities associated with inelastic intermediate states could, in principle, be attacked in the same way and additional arbitrary CDD poles can be added.

A different, but hopefully equivalent, method has been given by Cutkosky,[32] who showed how to determine the discontinuity in an arbitrary Feynman graph. The method involves replacing the internal propagators $(M^2 - p^2)^{-1}$ responsible for the discontinuity by $i\pi\delta(M^2 - p^2)$; the reader is referred to Cutkosky's papers for details. In simple cases such as elastic intermediate states, Cutkosky's prescription is explicitly equivalent to the relation (5-17) that we derived from unitarity.

In practice, inelastic processes involving more than two particles are very complicated and only limited progress has been made in understanding them. Therefore, we shall confine ourselves largely to reactions with two incoming and two outgoing particles.

Specializing further, imagine we have an elastic reaction for which all spectral functions are known <u>except</u> the double spectral function associated with elastic intermediate states in this channel.[33] The motivation for organizing our thoughts this way is to parallel non-relativistic potential scattering where the term with no elastic cuts in s (the potential) was given, and the rest followed from unitarity. The known part of the t-cut then, ignoring subtractions, is given by

$$V_I^{II}(t,s) = A_t(t,s) - \frac{1}{\pi} \int ds' \, \frac{A_{st}^{I(e\ell)}(s',t)}{s' - s} \tag{6-1}$$

where we label the s, t, and u-channels by I, II, and III respectively. $A_{st}^{I(e\ell)}$ is the double spectral function with an elastic intermediate state in channel I. The discontinuity V_I^{II} serves as weight function for the generalized potential contributed by the cut in channel II to channel I. It includes terms such as Fig. (5-6) with inelastic intermediate states in channel I, but the "box diagram", for example, is not included because it has an elastic intermediate state in the s-channel.

In the same spirit, the given u-cut will be called V_I^{III}, the generalized potential supplied by channel III to channel I:

$$V_I^{III}(u,s) = A_u(u,s) - \frac{1}{\pi} \int \frac{ds'}{s'-s} \, A_{su}^{I(e\ell)}(s',u) \quad . \tag{6-2}$$

In accordance with the usual significance of direct and exchange forces, V_I^{II} is identified as a "direct" potential and V_I^{III} as an "exchange" potential. For example, in πN scattering, two pion exchange would contribute to the direct potential and nucleon exchange contributes to the exchange potential.

Let us ignore spin as usual, and diagonalize any internal quantum numbers (isotopic spin, strangeness, etc.) in the s-channel. In the equal mass case, the given cuts run from $t = 4m^2$ to $t = \infty$, and $u = 4m^2$ to $u = \infty$, respectively. From the earlier discussion of the Mandelstam representation, we recall that the t and u-cuts, together with elastic unitarity in the s-channel, necessitate the double spectral functions:

$$A_{st}^{I(e\ell)}(s,t) = \frac{1}{\pi q_s \sqrt{s}} \left[\iint \frac{dt'\, dt''\, A_t^*(t',s)\, A_t(t'',s)}{K^{1/2}(q_s^{\,2}, t, t', t'')} + \iint \frac{du'\, du''\, A_u^*(u',s)\, A_u(u'',s)}{K^{1/2}(q_s^{\,2}, t, u', u'')} \right] , \qquad (6\text{-}3)$$

$$A_{su}^{I(e\ell)}(s,u) = \frac{1}{\pi q_s \sqrt{s}} \left[\iint \frac{dt'\, du''\, A_t^*(t',s)\, A_u(u',s)}{K^{1/2}(q_s^{\,2}, u, t', u')} + \iint \frac{du'\, dt'\, A_u^*(u',s)\, A_t(t',s)}{K^{1/2}(q_s^{\,2}, u, u', t')} \right] . \qquad (6\text{-}4)$$

K has already been given in Eq. (4-11). As usual, the range of integration in (6-3) and (6-4) is restricted to the region in which K is positive, and the elastic double spectral functions have curved boundaries with asymptotes $s = 4m^2$, $t = 16m^2$, and $s = 4m^2$, $u = 16m^2$, respectively. To start the calculation one can approximate A_t and A_u by the respective potentials. After an iteration, the t and u cuts become:

$$A_t = V_I^{II}(t,s) + \frac{1}{\pi} \int ds' \frac{A_{st}^{I(e\ell)}(s',t)}{s' - s} , \quad (6\text{-}5)$$

$$A_u = V_I^{III}(u,s) + \frac{1}{\pi} \int ds' \frac{A_{su}^{I(e\ell)}(s',u)}{s' - s} . \quad (6\text{-}6)$$

Here the newly calculated parts of A_t and A_u have cuts beginning at $t = (4m)^2$, $u = (4m)^2$, and when these are inserted into (6-3) and (6-4) they produce further cuts of $A_{st}^{I(e\ell)}$, $A_{su}^{I(e\ell)}$ beginning at $t = (6m)^2$, $u = (6m)^2$. Higher iterations produce cuts beginning at $t = (8m)^2$, $t = (10m)^2$, etc. In terms of diagrams, whatever particles were exchanged in the potential are exchanged twice in the first iteration, three times in the next iteration, and so forth.

If one considers non-relativistic scattering by a superposition of Yukawa direct and exchange potentials

$$V_{direct}(r) = - \frac{1}{2m^2} \int dt \, \rho_{dir}(t) \frac{e^{-r\sqrt{t}}}{r} , \quad (6\text{-}7)$$

$$V_{exchange}(r) = - \frac{1}{2m^2} \int du \, \rho_{ex}(u) \frac{e^{-r\sqrt{u}}}{r} , \quad (6\text{-}8)$$

then, except for trivial questions of normalization, if V_I^{II} is replaced by ρ_{dir} and V_I^{III} by ρ_{ex}, the equations determining the double spectral functions differ from (6-3) and (6-4) only in the replacement of the factor $\sqrt{s}$ by 2m. Thus our generalized potentials determine the dynamics in much the same way as an ordinary potential. The special relativistic features are that the generalized potential is energy-dependent and becomes complex above inelastic threshold, where the imaginary part is:

$$A_{st}^{I(in)} = A_{st} - A_{st}^{I(e\ell)} \quad . \tag{6-9}$$

In what limit does one regain the Schrödinger equation? Or in other words, in what limit does the Mandelstam representation reduce to its non-relativistic form? One necessary condition is $(s - 4m^2) << 4m^2$; in this limit the kinematic factor $\sqrt{s} \simeq 2m$, the energy dependence of the potential can be ignored, and below inelastic threshold the potential is real. But through the integration over large s' in (6-5), low energies are connected to high energies where the full relativistic equation is needed. One can always take the difference between relativistic and non-relativistic values of the integral and add it to the potential; this allows the integral to be expressed in the non-relativistic way but means the potential is not known until the problem is completely solved. The Schrödinger equation emerges more naturally when the potential is sufficiently broad and shallow that the scattered particle ceases to feel it when the kinetic energy is raised to levels that are still non-relativistic. A classic example is atomic physics where the potential extends far beyond the Compton wave length of the electron and is quite shallow. In other words, the scale of low-energy atomic physics is set by the Bohr radius and the regions of relativistic scattering (at kinetic energies at least of order 10^5 eV) or crossed physical channels (at kinetic energies of order minus 10^9 eV) are so far away on this scale that they can be ignored. Low-energy nuclear physics, where the ratio of the range of the forces to the nuclear Compton wave length is only about seven, is more of a borderline case: the Schrödinger equation can be used but relativistic corrections are greater than in atomic physics.[34)]

Having established the connection between the Mandelstam representation and more familiar potential theory, we can greatly enrich our physical intuition for relativistic scattering by calling on potential analogies. We shall do so in describing some of the useful approximations to the Mandelstam representation, as well as their limitations. Later, when considerations of asymptotic behavior finally lead to an impasse between unitarity and the existence of particles with spin > 1, we shall borrow the notion of Regge poles from potential theory to escape the impasse.

VII. APPROXIMATIONS TO THE MANDELSTAM REPRESENTATION: POLOLOGY AND NEARBY CUTS

The central theme of most approximations to dispersion relations has been the dominance of nearby singularities. Mathematically, the idea is simply that a pole term $\rho/\pi(t_o-t)$ is bigger and varies more rapidly when $|t_o-t|$ is small than when it is large, and similarly for cut terms. Physically, we recall from the discussion of the N/D method that nearby singularities, such as $\rho/\pi(t_o-t)$ with small t_o, are associated with long range forces. Long range contributions to the potential are important because:

(a) In peripheral collisions the incoming particle sees only the long range part of the potential. These collisions may be singled out by looking at small angles. Mathematically, the momentum transfer $t = -2q_s^2\,(1 - \cos\Theta)$ is then small, and in the potential

$$\frac{1}{\pi}\int_{t_{min}}^{\infty}\frac{\rho(t')\,dt'}{t'-t}\quad, \tag{7-1}$$

small t' are especially important.

(b) For a strong potential of radius R, the geometrical value πR^2 gives a fairly good estimate of the cross section. The outer part of the potential provides most of the geometrical cross section, so it tends to dominate the total cross section as well as small angle scattering.

In addition to these arguments, the long-range part of the generalized potential is on especially firm theoretical ground because attempts to verify the Mandelstam representation from field theory made more progress at small t, where scattering in the t-channel is elastic, than at large t. Finally, the replacement of the whole amplitude by one or several poles (polology) offers the irresistable advantage that one doesn't have to consider the double spectral function at all!

In the simplest applications of polology, for example in $N + N \to N + N$, one keeps the pole at $t = m_\pi^2$ and drops the complicated cut at $t > 4m_\pi^2$. We have seen that iteration of a potential with a singularity at $t = m_\pi^2$ leads to an elastic double spectral function $A_{st}^{I(e\ell)}$ with threshold at $t = (2m_\pi)^2$. Since $A_{st}^{I(e\ell)}$ starts at a larger t than the pole term, it can be dropped by the same argument we used on the shorter range part of the potential.

It is not surprising if the pole approximation fails at $t \lesssim -4m_\pi^2$ where the cut $t \geq 4m_\pi^2$ is less than twice as "far away" at the pole at $t = m_\pi^2$. In the N-N case, there are problems even at smaller t:

(a) Forward scattering contains a diffraction peak. This means that the neglected cuts are especially important at small t.

(b) Forward p-p scattering has a Coulomb term.

(c) Because a nucleon undergoing no momentum transfer cannot emit a negative parity pion, the amplitude actually behaves like $tg^2/(m_\pi^2 - t)$ which is not so easy to see at small t.

Difficulty (b) can be eliminated by using neutrons or leaving out the narrow Coulomb peak. Difficulty (a) can be eliminated by looking at backward scattering (a pole in u). Doing so, we obtain an expression for the cross section

$$\frac{d\sigma}{du} = \frac{C_1(s,t,u)}{(m_\pi^2-u)^2} + \frac{C_2(s,t,u)}{m_\pi^2 - u} + C_3(s,t,u) \quad . \tag{7-2}$$

The C's are regular at $u = m_\pi^2$. The first term involves the pole in both matrix elements; the second term is an interference term. Equation (7-2) can be treated in several different ways:

(i) Look for the pole term in the physical region $u = -2q_s^2\ (1+\cos\theta) \leq 0$. Difficulty (c) above also applies to the u variable and makes this somewhat hard to do.

(ii) Extrapolate $(m_\pi^2 - u)^2\ d\sigma/du$ from physical $u \leq 0$, where there is data, to $u = m_\pi^2$. In this way, the residue of the pole can be determined.[35)] In the case at hand, the residue is simply related to the renormalized pion-nucleon coupling constant, and the result is consistent with other determinations of this coupling constant. Unfortunately, accuracy is again limited by difficulty (c) above and also by the fact that other singularities are also contributing in the physical region. In fact, we see quite generally that the approximation can work only if the residue of the pole is at least of the same magnitude as the integrated discontinuities of the other nearbye singularities. The pole is most likely to stand out if it lies considerably closer to the physical region than the cut in u; p-p scattering is favorable because the pole at $u = m_\pi^2$ is close compared to the branch point at $u = 4m_\pi^2$, whereas in nucleon-hyperon scattering, the pole at $u = m_k^2$ is nearly as far away as the branch point at $u = (m_k + m_\pi)^2$.

(iii) Use the pole terms in t and u to determine the high partial waves which see only the outer potential $\left[\ell \gtrsim qR\right]$, and determine the low partial waves separately by phenomenology or by including shorter range singularities. This method has been especially successful in $N + N \rightarrow N + N$.[36]

Recently polology has been applied with considerable success to high-energy inelastic processes. Consider, for example,

$$N + N \rightarrow N + N^* \tag{7-3}$$

where N^* is the 3-3 resonance. At small t and energies of a couple of BeV, the one-pion exchange model fits the data fairly well.[37]

It should be clear by now that polology works only at small momentum transfers, and even then only under favorable circumstances. The logical next step is to include the intermediate range potential. For example, in N-N scattering, $4m_\pi^2 \leq t \leq 9m_\pi^2$ is still a relatively simple region representing elastic scattering in the t-channel. This region is especially easy to treat if elastic scattering in the t-channel is dominated by one or several narrow resonances, for then the resonances can be approximated by particles and one can again do polology and ignore the double spectral function. Three-particle exchange is more complicated unless at least two of the particles resonate, allowing a reduction to exchange of not more than two objects.

For purposes of illustration, consider the scattering of spinless, identical-mass particles which exchange a narrow P-wave resonance. The full amplitude has the partial wave expansion

$$A = \frac{\sqrt{q_t^2 + m^2}}{q_t} \sum_{\ell=0}^{\infty} (2\ell+1)\, e^{i\delta_\ell} \sin \delta_\ell \, P_\ell (\cos \Theta_t) \tag{7-4}$$

in the t-channel, and the P-wave in this channel contributes a cut

$$A_t = \frac{\sqrt{q_t^2 + m^2}}{q_t} \, 3 \sin^2\delta_1 \, \cos \Theta_t \tag{7-5}$$

in the elastic region. Let the resonance occur at $t = t_R$ with full width Γ; for small Γ, the cut can be approximated by

$$A_t \sim \frac{\sqrt{q_{t_R}^2 + m^2}}{q_{t_R}} \, 3 \, \delta (t - t_R) \, \Gamma \, \cos \Theta_{t_R} \tag{7-6}$$

which gives the same value as a Breit-Wigner dependence when integrated over. The P-wave exchange contributes a potential

$$\frac{1}{\pi} \int \frac{dt' \, A_t(t')}{t' - t} = \frac{C \cos \Theta_{t_R}}{t_R - t} = \frac{C \left\{ - 1 - \frac{s}{2q_{t_R}^2} \right\}}{t_R + 2q_s^2 \, (1 - \cos \Theta_s)} \tag{7-7}$$

which contributes to the S-wave in the s-channel:

$$A_o(s) = \frac{1}{2} \int_{-1}^{1} d \cos \Theta_s \, P_o \, (\cos \Theta_s) \, \frac{C \cos \Theta_{t_R}}{t_R - t}$$

$$= \frac{C}{4q_s^2} \left\{ - 1 - \frac{s}{2q_{t_R}^2} \right\} \, \ell n \left(1 + \frac{4q_s^2}{t_R} \right) \quad . \tag{7-8}$$

At large s one finds

$$A_0 \sim -\frac{C}{2q_{t_R}^2} \ell n \frac{s}{t_R} \tag{7-9}$$

whereas the unitarity bound for

$$A_0 = \frac{\sqrt{q_s^2 + m_\pi^2}}{q_s} \frac{e^{2i\delta_0} - 1}{2i} \tag{7-10}$$

at large s is unity. Of course, if one is interested only in Born approximations at low energy, Eq. (7-8) is all right. But attempts to iterate (7-8) by the N/D method lead to divergences, because the unitarity bound has been exceeded. Note that if a $J = 0$ particle had been exchanged, the $\cos \theta_t$ factor in (7-5) would have been absent and A_0 would behave asymptotically like $s^{-1} \ell n\, s$. On the other hand, exchange of a $J = 2$ particle leads to worse trouble than the P-wave did. These results recall the situation in field theory where $J = 0$ particles are renormalizable, $J = 1$ particles are logarithmically divergent except in certain cases like the photon where the divergent terms cancel due to symmetries,* and higher spin particles are more divergent.

---

*For exchange of an uncharged spin one particle, the N/D method diverges only because it violates crossing symmetry. In treatments which preserve crossing symmetry, the divergences cancel. If the spin one particle is charged, however, the divergences do <u>not</u> cancel.

What can be done about divergences? The simplest remedy is to cut them off, by making subtractions in the N/D method for example. The additional parameters introduced by the cut-off or subtraction represent effects from large s or large t. A more ambitious approach is to try to calculate the large s and t effects properly instead of adding arbitrary parameters. This line of approach has led to the strip approximation and Regge poles.

A practical example of the above considerations, only slightly complicated by the addition of isotopic spin, is $\pi + \pi \to \pi + \pi$. The π-π reaction is of great importance, both because it is relatively simple to study theoretically and because it provides long-range forces for other reactions involving heavier particles. The potential with isotopic spin T in the s-channel receives a weight function

$$\rho^{T} = \sum_{T'} \beta_{TT'} \, A_t^{(e\ell)T'} \tag{7-11}$$

from exchange of elastic states with isotopic spin $T' = 0, 1, 2$. The crossing matrix has the form[7]

$$\beta_{TT'} = \begin{pmatrix} 1/3 & 1 & 5/3 \\ 1/3 & 1/2 & -5/6 \\ 1/3 & -1/2 & 1/6 \end{pmatrix} . \tag{7-12}$$

Chew, Mandelstam, and Noyes[38] initiated the study of this problem. They estimated the S-waves by iterating the $\lambda \phi_\pi^4$ interaction, and then used S-wave exchange as a potential for the s-channel. The procedure converged rapidly and the potential produced very little scattering in the higher angular momentum states, indicating that the use of only S-wave exchange in the low-energy potential was qualitatively consistent.

This first treatment of π-π scattering was unsatisfactory because it failed to produce the P-wave resonance (now called the ρ meson), whose existence was already suspected at that time from analysis of nucleon electromagnetic structure.[39] So Chew and Mandelstam[3] asked what would happen if a P-wave resonance were exchanged. Because of the symmetry of the two-pion state, such a resonance necessarily has $T = 1$. The $+ 1/2$ term in the middle of the crossing matrix (7-12) means that exchange of the resonance supplies an attractive force to the $T = 1$ state in the s-channel, and Chew and Mandelstam showed the attraction was adequate for producing a $T = 1, J = 1$ resonance consistent with the width and mass of the exchanged one. This kind of reasoning, based on self-consistency rather than on iterations of the Lagrangian, is called the "bootstrap method".

As usual, the P-wave resonance necessitated a high-energy cut-off, so the Chew-Mandelstam solution contained at least two arbitrary parameters.

Another example of the potential approach is provided by π-N scattering.* In Chew-Low theory,[42] the potential was provided mainly by exchange of the nucleon, with some corrections from exchange of the 3-3 resonance. In its original static form, the theory was highly divergent, but in a relativistic treatment,[43,44] one finds that the nucleon exchange is convergent and it is only the corrections due to exchange of higher spins (e.g., the $T = 3/2$, $J = 3/2$ resonance) that are divergent. The direct potential due to exchange of the ρ meson seems to have little effect on the 3-3 resonance[44] but is important for understanding the difference between $T = 1/2$ and $T = 3/2$ states in some of the smaller phase shifts.[45]

---

*In reactions involving particles with spin, the full amplitude is the sum of several independent invariant functions multiplied by spin matrices such as $\gamma \cdot p$. Goldberger, Grisaru, McDowell, and Wong,[40] and Hearn[41] have given methods for choosing the spin matrices in such a way that the invariant functions multiplying them have only the Mandelstam singularities. For any function A, which has only Mandelstam singularities, one can devise many functions with additional "kinematic" singularities (e.g., $B = \sqrt{s}\, A$ has a kinematic branch point at $s = 0$), but of course it is desirable to avoid unnecessary singularities whenever possible.

So much for the potential approach which ignores the double spectral function and concentrates on exchange of individual particles and resonances. This approach has its limitations:

(a) It is restricted to low energies. At $4m^2 \leq s \leq 16m^2$ for example, the direct potential is still evaluated near the physical region for the t-channel, so if a P-wave dominates the t-channel, it probably also dominates the direct potential, but at large s the direct potential is evaluated far from the physical t-channel and may no longer have such a simple relation to it.

(b) Inelastic scattering is not treated properly.

(c) Every time another partial wave with spin ≥ 1 is exchanged, we get another divergence.

(c) The method does not guarantee crossing symmetries.

Some of these difficulties are overcome, and others are at least illuminated, by the strip approximation.

VIII. THE STRIP APPROXIMATION

The strip approximation,[4,46] like previous approximations, is based on the neglect of certain short-range effects. The elastic double spectral function is calculated in each channel; the double spectral functions which are inelastic in each channel are not calculated. In terms of diagrams, this means we keep Figs. 8-1(a)(b), but neglect Fig. 8-1(c). Figure 8-1(a) represents a long-range force in the s-channel, Fig. 8-1(b) represents a long-range force in the t-channel, and the neglected Fig. 8-1(c) represents a short-range force in each channel.

The name "strip approximation" comes from the Mandelstam plot, Fig. 8-2. In the strips $4 < s < 16$, $4 < t < 16$, $4 < u < 16$ (in units m_π^2), the elastic unitarity condition used to calculate the double spectral function is exact. In the interior regions such as $s > 16$, $t > 16$, it is only approximate. The equations used in each channel to calculate the elastic double spectral function are just (5-17), etc. To cross from one channel to another in the presence of isotopic spin, relations like (7-11) are used.

How does this approximation overcome limitations of the previous approaches?

(a) The method is not restricted to low energies. It has some validity in any region near one of the strips where unitarity is treated exactly. From Fig. 8-2, we see that the physical regions where the method applies are strips of small direct or exchange momentum but arbitrary energy in each channel.

(b) Inelastic scattering is still not treated properly, but at least some of its effects are included (however, the neglected terms are very important!). In Fig. 8-1(a), we see what kind of terms are included: they are diffraction terms, obtained by iteration of the one-pion exchange contribution to inelastic events. Note the interpretation of the same diagrams in the t-channel. In addition to the two-pion exchange potential, we are keeping its iterations -- four-pion exchange, six-pion exchange, and so on.

(c) Some of the divergences associated with exchange of high partial waves arose from the use of the Legendre series expansion outside of its region of convergence. The improper series expansion is avoided by the strip approximation, so the divergences do not appear.

For example, suppose the weight function ρ_t of the generalized potential has the form

$$\rho_t = \frac{1}{\pi} \int_{16m^2}^{\infty} \frac{ds' \, F(s',t)}{s' - s} \quad . \tag{8-1}$$

For simplicity, consider $F(s',t) = \pi \, \delta \, (s' - s_o) \, G(t)$, which leads to

$$\rho_t = \frac{G(t)}{s_o - s} \quad . \tag{8-2}$$

This expression is an example of what one finds by using the strip approximation; the important point is that it converges at large s.

From (8-2) one can calculate the partial wave

$$A_{\ell t}(t) = \frac{1}{2} \int_{-1}^{1} d \cos \Theta_t \, P_\ell (\cos \Theta_t) \frac{G(t)}{s_o + 2q_t^2 (1 + \cos \Theta_t)} \tag{8-3}$$

in the t-channel. In connection with the potential for the s-channel, let us exchange the partial waves $A_{\ell t}(t)$ up to $\ell = N$:

$$I_n = \sum_{\ell=0}^{N} (2\ell + 1) A_{\ell t}(t) P_\ell (\cos \Theta_t) \quad . \tag{8-4}$$

This series is, of course, convergent for $-1 \leq \cos \Theta_t \leq 1$. But as $\cos \Theta_t \to \infty$ at fixed t (i.e., as $s = -2q_t^2 (1 + \cos \Theta_t) \to \infty$), the Legendre series expansion diverges $(P_\ell (\cos \Theta_t) \sim (\cos \Theta_t)^\ell \sim s^\ell)$. Thus $I_N \sim s^N$, whereas the complete expression (8-2) behaves like s^{-1} at large s. More precisely, the expansion converges in an ellipse[47] with focii $\cos \Theta_t = \pm 1$, bounded by the singularity at $s = s_o$. Outside the ellipse, the function can be continued in the form $(s - s_o)^{-1}$. In the strip approximation, this is accomplished because the potential is given its proper discontinuity at s above inelastic threshold, rather than keeping only low partial waves in the t-channel. Thus, when <u>all</u> partial waves are exchanged, the divergence difficulty associated with the exchange of any single partial wave is avoided.

The exchange of partial waves containing resonances or bound states requires special discussion, because these partial waves have additional poles, on or near the physical sheet, which are not manifest in the double spectral terms. This problem will be treated later in connection with Regge poles.

(d) The strip approximation treats each channel in the same spirit, and can therefore guarantee crossing symmetry.

To partially offset these advantages, the strip approximation is much more complicated than its predecessors. Partly for this reason, few calculations have been carried out with it in practice. Other reasons are that inelastic effects are still only partially accounted for and resonances or bound states with $J \geq 1$ still present divergence difficulties. Actually the strip approximation performed its greatest service to date by focussing attention on the asymptotic properties of the scattering amplitude.

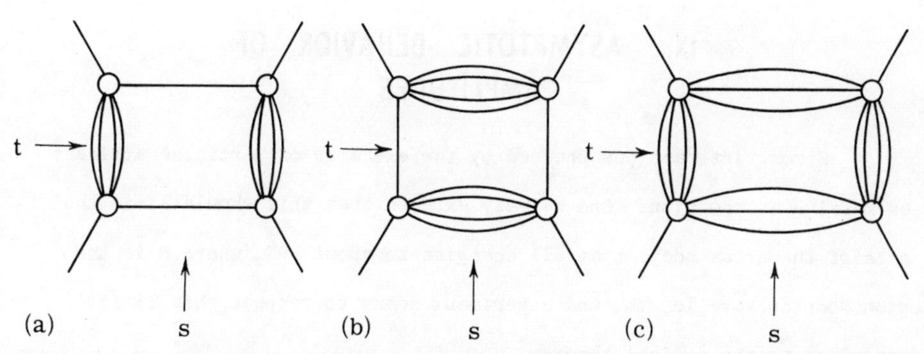

Figure 8-1 Cutkosky diagrams with two-particle intermediate states in: (a) the t-channel, (b) the s-channel, (c) neither channel.

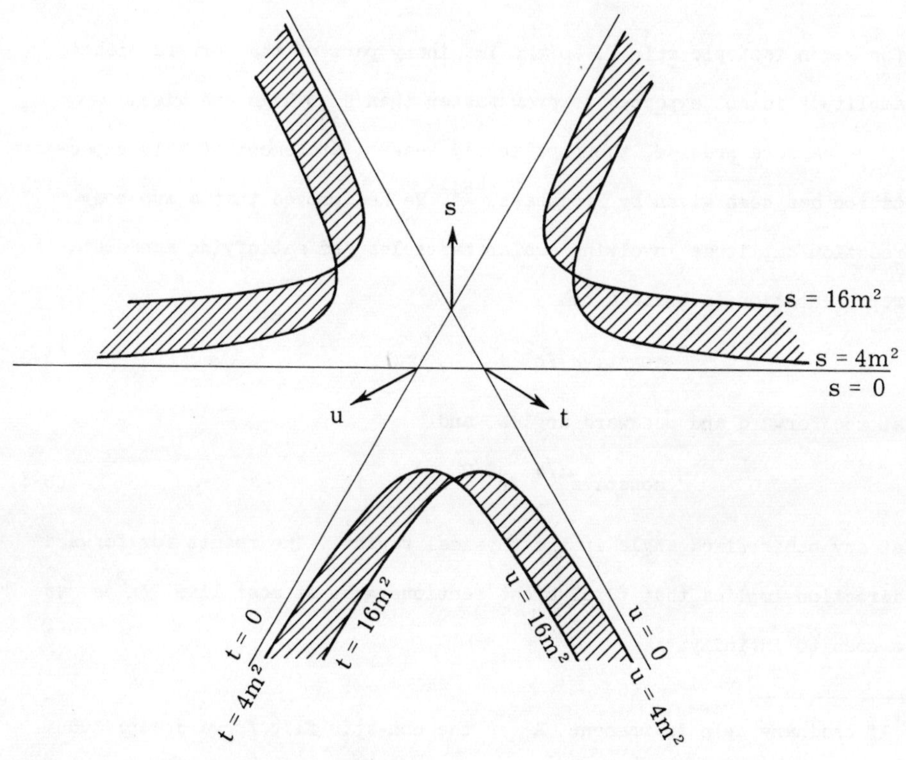

Figure 8-2 Mandelstam plot of the physical and unphysical regions for pion-pion scattering, with the strips shaded.

IX. ASYMPTOTIC BEHAVIOR OF AMPLITUDES

Strong interactions proceed by the exchange of particles at least as massive as the pion. One naively expects that this should limit the size of the cross section at all energies to about πR^2, where R is the pion Compton wave length, and experiment seems to respect this limit. According to the optical theorem*

$$\text{Im}\, A^T(s,0) = A_s^T(s,0) = \frac{q_s\, s^{1/2}}{8\pi}\, \sigma_{tot}^T(s) \tag{9-1}$$

for given isotopic spin T, so the imaginary part of the forward elastic amplitude is not expected to grow faster than s at high energies.

A more precise, though slightly weaker, statement of this expectation has been given by Froissart.[48] He has proved that a two-body reaction amplitude involving scalar particles and satisfying Mandelstam's representation is bounded by

$$\text{const.}\; s\, \ell n^2\, s \tag{9-2}$$

at the forward and backward angles, and

$$\text{const.}\; s^{3/4}\, \ell n^{3/2}\, s \tag{9-3}$$

at any other fixed angle in the physical region. The result for forward direction implies that total cross sections grow at most like $\ell n^2\, s$ as s goes to infinity.

---

*If ordinary spin is present, A^T is the non-spin flip forward amplitude.

For the details of Froissart's proof, the reader is referred to his paper. One can get an intuitive idea why the amplitude is bounded from an example also given by Froissart: Two particles interact by means of a Yukawa potential $g \frac{e^{-mr}}{r}$. If a is the impact parameter, the total interaction seen by a particle for large a is essentially controlled by $g\,e^{-ma}$. If this is small compared to one, there will be practically no scattering. If $g\,e^{-ma}$ is large compared to one, there will be practically complete scattering. So the cross section will be essentially determined by the value $a = \frac{1}{m} \ln g$ where $g\,e^{-ma} = 1$. It is $\sigma \cong \frac{\pi}{m^2} \ln^2 g$. If we now assume that g is a function of the energy, and increases like a power of the energy (which is all that is allowed by the Mandelstam representation), then σ will vary at most like the squared logarithm of the energy.

It is interesting that the asymptotic behavior of amplitudes observed in nature is so close to Froissart's upper limit. More will be said about this later.

Froissart's bound on the amplitude in the physical region leads to important limitations on the number of arbitrary subtraction terms. A term

$$P_\ell (\cos \Theta_t)\, f(t) \quad , \tag{9-4}$$

for example, behaves like s^ℓ at large s because of the relation

$$\cos \Theta_t = -1 - \frac{s}{2q_t^2} \quad . \tag{9-5}$$

Thus any subtraction term with $\ell > 1$ individually violates the Froissart bound. Froissart proceeded to show that a finite number of subtraction terms cannot cancel in such a way as to restore the bound. The other possible cancellation -- between the subtraction terms and the double spectral function terms -- is ruled out if the subtractions are independent. Since CDD poles provide our mechanism for producing subtractions, the restriction of arbitrary subtractions to $J = 0, 1/2$, and 1 appears to imply that CDD poles can be introduced only in these low partial waves.* This is very close to the results of renormalization theory, where particles with $J > 1$ (and often $J = 1$) do not lead to renormalizable interactions, and in both cases the results are achieved by arguments on asymptotic power behavior. Froissart's conclusions do differ in being independent of perturbation theory, and are more lenient in allowing

---

*Through crossing relations, however, a CDD pole affects the double spectral functions as well as the partial wave where it is originally introduced, so it is not immediately apparent that the partial wave becomes independent of the double spectral function. In π-N scattering with the usual renormalizable interaction, the $J = 1/2$, $T = 1/2$, π-N state is indeed represented by an independent subtraction term. But for a suggestion, unresolved at the present time, that this may not be the case when spin one particles are present, see Gell-Mann and Goldberger.[49)]

charged $J = 1$ particles whose interactions cannot be renormalized. When charged $J = 1$ particles are inserted into the S-matrix and treated in detail, however, they produce divergences just as in field theory.

The agreement between S-matrix theory and renormalization theory on what independent parameters are permitted is reassuring, and suggests that any states with $J > 1$ must be composite, whereas states with $J \leq 1/2$ (and certain neutral states with $J = 1$) may be either composite or elementary. Of course, many states here classified as composite exist in nature -- the deuteron, pion-nucleon resonances, ρ meson, etc. But a crisis develops when we ask how such composite states are to be described in the Mandelstam representation. The situation is clearest for stable particles, which are represented by poles on the physical sheet. The poles are, of course, not part of the double spectral function and must be written as separate terms of the form

$$g^2 P_\ell (\cos \Theta_s) \frac{1}{m^2 - s} \quad . \tag{9-6}$$

But if $\ell \geq 1$, these terms individually violate the Froissart bound. Resonant partial waves with $\ell \geq 1$ fare not much better; their poles are on the unphysical sheet but it is not obvious that the double spectral function implies such poles.

To avert the crisis, we shall go back to properties of composite states discovered and established by Regge for non-relativistic scattering. These properties will then be conjectured to hold for the relativistic case. The result will be that bound states or resonance poles are not independent of the double spectral function, but are meshed together in such a way that states of $\ell \geq 1$ are consistent with the Froissart limit.

X. REGGE POLES IN NON-RELATIVISTIC SCATTERING

In order to introduce the idea of Regge poles,* it is helpful to think of an ordinary attractive potential. If the attraction is sufficiently large, an S-wave bound state is obtained at E_S. For a purely attractive well, the radial wave function has no nodes, since a slowly varying radial behavior minimizes kinetic energy. An even larger attraction can overcome the centrifugal barrier for P-waves, and a P-wave bound state or resonance results at an energy $E_P > E_S$. To minimize the kinetic energy, it has the same number of radial nodes as did the S-wave. As the attraction is further increased, a whole family of related bound states or resonances can be obtained, with increasing angular momentum and energy $(\ldots E_D > E_P > E_S)$ but the same radial structure. A second S-wave bound state with less advantageous radial structure (e.g., an additional radial node) also appears. It has energy $E_{S'} > E_S$, and represents the start of a second family which can also spread to higher ℓ $(\ldots E_{D'} > E_{P'} > E_{S'})$. Later, more and more families can appear. Atomic and nuclear physics are full of examples, such as the Bohr atom (Chapter 11).

Regge poles provide an alternative description of this "family" phenomenon. In atomic and nuclear physics, this alternative description is instructive but has not led thus far to new physical applications. The new applications have come in the conjectured extension of Regge poles to essentially relativistic phenomena, where the Schrödinger

---

*The reader who wishes to consult the original sources will find it easiest to begin with the paper by Bottino, Longoni, and Regge.[25]

equation no longer applies. Therefore, before describing the exact statements that can be made for non-relativistic scattering, it is appropriate to sketch briefly the applications conjectured for relativistic scattering:

i) We suppose that many, perhaps all, strongly interacting particles, such as n, p, π, the 3-3 resonance, etc., are bound states or resonances held together by attractive potentials. For example, suppose the Σ with baryon number one, strangeness minus one, and isotopic spin one is a bound state of $\Lambda + \pi$. Then it is possible to have a family of particles with these quantum numbers and increasing ℓ, and technically the family is described by a Regge pole. The spacing in energy between members of the family can be estimated from the size of the centrifugal barrier

$$V_c = \frac{\hbar^2 \, \ell(\ell+1)}{2mr^2} \quad . \tag{10-1}$$

Inserting $m \simeq m_\pi$ for the reduced mass of the bound $\Lambda\pi$ system, and $r \leq 10^{-13}$ cm for the radius of the presumed attractive potential, we find that V_c increases by hundreds of MeV as ℓ increases by one unit. Thus the members of the family are widely spaced (in atomic and nuclear physics, the radius was larger and the spacing much closer), and all but the lowest member should be unstable. At the present time, resonances several hundred MeV above the lowest state have been found in this and many other channels, but in most cases we do not yet have definitive spin-parity assignments and thus cannot verify whether they belong to Regge families.

ii) Relativistic scattering is often described in terms of particle exchange: the proton-proton force comes from π exchange, plus ρ exchange, plus exchange of heavier objects. At high energies this description often has the practical drawback of not explaining observed cross sections. There is also a difficulty of principle -- exchange of particles with spin greater than one, or of charged particles with spin one, leads to divergences.

An alternative suggested by Regge pole theory is to exchange (π + any members of the same family with higher ℓ + certain non-resonant exchanges, all adding up to the pion Regge pole) + (ρ + any other members of the ρ family + other non-resonant exchanges adding up to the ρ Regge pole) + ... This allows us to explain the data more readily and provides a more convergent theory, since the divergences associated with individual high-spin members of a family turn out to cancel when the whole family is added together appropriately.

Thus motivated, we return to non-relativistic scattering. The radial Schrödinger equation ($h = c = 2m = 1$)

$$- \frac{d^2\psi}{dr^2} + \frac{\ell(\ell+1)}{r^2} \psi + V\psi - E\psi = 0 \tag{10-2}$$

will be used with the usual boundary condition

$$\psi \underset{r \to 0}{\sim} r^{\ell+1} \quad . \tag{10-3}$$

Above threshold ψ has the asymptotic behavior

$$\psi \underset{r \to \infty}{\sim} e^{-iqr} - e^{-i\pi \ell} \; S \; e^{+iqr} \tag{10-4}$$

where

$$S \equiv e^{2i\delta(\ell,E)} \quad . \tag{10-5}$$

At a pole of S, the second term in (10-4) is infinitely greater than the first term, and a pure outgoing wave results. Below threshold at $q^2 < 0$, $q = i\,|q|$, Eq. (10-4) takes the form

$$\psi \underset{r \to \infty}{\sim} e^{|q|r} - e^{-i\pi \ell} \; S \; e^{-|q|r} \quad . \tag{10-6}$$

Here a pole of S favors the decreasing exponential component by an infinite factor, resulting in a normalizable bound state.* Of course, S could also become infinite by means of higher order poles or branch points, but in practice simple poles are most important and we confine our attention to that case.

At a bound S-state, then, the S-matrix for $\ell = 0$ has a pole in the energy variable. A family of bound states with increasing angular momentum and energy is represented by a family of poles of the S-matrix. That is the picture for the physical, positive integer values of ℓ.

Now consider the radial Schrödinger equation (10-2) at arbitrary complex ℓ, still imposing the boundary condition (10-3). The solutions at non-integer ℓ are no longer physical states, for the usual reason

---

*As discussed in Chapter 2, bound states also imply $S = 0$ at $q = -i\,|q|$, but that is not of interest to us here.

that the angular dependence exhibits singularities, but nevertheless the radial equation poses a well-defined mathematical problem. Below threshold, one finds that the "bound state" condition $\psi \sim \exp(-|q|\, r)$ has a whole family of solutions. As ℓ is increased continuously, the centrifugal barrier increases continuously and the binding energy of the solutions naturally decreases. These solutions interpolate smoothly between the physical bound states at integer ℓ. Since Eq. (10-6) still holds, the whole family of solutions satisfying $\psi \sim \exp(-|q|\, r)$ is described by the continuous movement of a pole of $S(\ell, E)$, and physical bound states occur at the discrete intervals where this pole passes through integer ℓ. The moving pole is called a "Regge pole". Above threshold, one finds that the pole continues to move as the energy varies, and corresponds to an outgoing wave boundary condition.

Certain conditions on the positions of the poles follow from very general arguments. Consider the radial Schrödinger equation (10-2) and its complex conjugate at real V and E,

$$-\frac{d^2\psi^*}{dr^2} + \frac{\ell^*(\ell^*+1)}{r^2}\psi^* + V\psi^* - E\psi^* = 0 \quad . \tag{10-7}$$

The difference of (10-2) times ψ^* and ψ times (10-7) is

$$-\frac{d^2\psi}{dr^2}\psi^* + \psi\frac{d^2\psi^*}{dr^2} + \frac{[\ell(\ell+1) - \ell^*(\ell^*+1)]}{r^2}\psi^*\psi = 0 \tag{10-8}$$

which is equivalent to

$$\frac{d}{dr}\left(\psi \frac{d\psi^*}{dr} - \frac{d\psi}{dr}\psi^*\right) + 2i\,\ell_I\,(2\ell_R + 1)\,\frac{\psi^*\psi}{r^2} = 0 \qquad (10\text{-}9)$$

if we let $\ell = \ell_R + i\,\ell_I$. Integrating over r from 0 to ∞, one finds

$$\Big|_0^\infty \left(\psi \frac{d\psi^*}{dr} - \frac{d\psi}{dr}\psi^*\right) + 2i\,\ell_I\,(2\ell_R + 1)\int_0^\infty \frac{dr\,\psi^*\psi}{r^2} = 0 \quad . \qquad (10\text{-}10)$$

Below threshold, the boundary conditions at 0 and ∞ are $\psi \sim r^{\ell+1}$ and $\psi \sim \exp(-|q|\,r)$, so the first term in (10-10) vanishes for $\mathrm{Re}\,\ell > -1/2$. The integral is positive definite, so ℓ_I must vanish for a normalizable bound state, and thus for a pole of S.

Above threshold, the outgoing wave condition for a pole of S gives $\psi \sim C\exp(iqr)$ and $\psi^* \sim C^*\exp(-iqr)$ at large r. The condition at small r is the same as before, so (10-10) reads

$$-2iq\,|C|^2 + 2i\,\ell_I\,(2\ell_R + 1)\int_0^\infty \frac{dr\,\psi^*\psi}{r^2} = 0 \quad . \qquad (10\text{-}11)$$

The factors q, $|C|^2$, $(2\ell_R + 1)$, and the integral are all positive so ℓ_I must be positive. To summarize, the poles of S at $\ell_R > -1/2$ lie on the real axis when below threshold, and above the real axis when above threshold, under very general conditions. ¶ Below threshold, Regge was also able to derive a simple relation for the motion of poles of ℓ as a function of energy. Starting with the Schrödinger equation in the form

$$D\psi = 0 \quad , \qquad (10\text{-}12)$$

$$D = -\frac{d^2}{dr^2} + \frac{(\ell + \frac{1}{2})^2 - \frac{1}{4}}{r^2} + V - E \quad , \qquad (10\text{-}13)$$

one finds

$$\psi \frac{dD}{dE} \psi + \psi D \frac{d\psi}{dE} = 0 \quad , \tag{10-14}$$

$$\frac{dD}{dE} = \frac{1}{r^2} \frac{d(\ell + \frac{1}{2})^2}{dE} - 1 \quad . \tag{10-15}$$

The manipulations

$$\psi D - D\psi = \frac{d^2}{dr^2} \psi - \psi \frac{d^2}{dr^2}$$

$$= \frac{d}{dr} \left[\frac{d\psi}{dr} - \frac{\psi d}{dr} \right] \tag{10-16}$$

permit us to write the integral over (10-14) in the form

$$\int_0^\infty dr\, \psi \frac{dD}{dE} \psi + \Big|_0^\infty \left[\frac{d\psi}{dr} \frac{d\psi}{dE} - \psi \frac{d^2}{dr\, dE} \psi \right] = 0 \quad . \tag{10-17}$$

In view of the boundary conditions $\psi \sim r^{\ell+1}$ and $\psi \sim \exp(-|q|\, r)$ at small and large r respectively, the last term in (10-17) vanishes for $\ell_R > -1/2$, leaving

$$\frac{d(\ell + \frac{1}{2})^2}{dE} = \frac{\int_0^\infty dr\, \psi^2}{\int_0^\infty \frac{dr\, \psi^2}{r^2}} > 0 \quad . \tag{10-18}$$

This result is physically reasonable: states of higher and higher angular momentum can be bound as the energy approaches threshold, and the rate of increase is greater for a system with a large radius.

Equation (10-18) also provides the answer to a puzzling question: how can a fixed potential V continue to provide bound states as the energy becomes more and more negative? What happens is that the centrifugal repulsion $\ell(\ell+1)/r^2$ decreases and eventually turns into an attraction as ℓ becomes negative. As E continues to grow more negative, we must call on this "centripetal attraction" more and more until $\ell = -1/2$. In many cases ℓ continues to move left of $-1/2$, but in this region the Regge poles do not seem to have such a direct physical interpretation. The special significance of $\ell_R = -1/2$ is that the irregular solution defined by

$$\psi \underset{r \to 0}{\sim} r^{-\ell} \tag{10-19}$$

crosses the regular solution we are using (Eq. (10-3)).

Precise statements about the cusp behavior of Regge poles at threshold, and **qualitative** statements about their movement above threshold, can also be made, but we defer these statements until the relationship of Regge poles to phase shifts and resonances has been explained. To do this, we must now consider the full scattering amplitude. The usual partial-wave expansion of the scattering amplitude is

$$f(q,z) = \frac{1}{q} \sum_{\ell=0}^{\infty} (2\ell+1) \left(\frac{e^{2i\delta_\ell} - 1}{2i} \right) P_\ell(z) \tag{10-20}$$

where $z = \cos\theta$. Instead of confining his attention to integer angular momenta as in (10-20) however, Regge transformed the scattering amplitude to a new representation that involved complex ℓ. Known as the "Sommerfeld-Watson transformation", this method had a history stretching over several decades* and had been used to study rainbows, propagation of radio waves around the earth, and scattering from various potentials. Regge's original contribution lay in understanding the special features of complex angular momenta for scattering from superpositions of Yukawa potentials -- the type of potential believed relevant to relativistic scattering -- and calling these features to the attention of high-energy physicists.

Among the factors in Eq. (10-20), $(2\ell+1)$ is easy to extend to complex ℓ and there are standard methods (to be outlined later) for extending $P_\ell(z)$. The remaining ℓ dependence is in the S-matrix $\exp(2i\delta_\ell)$, which we have defined in terms of the solution of the radial Schrödinger equation (10-2) with boundary conditions (10-3) and asymptotic behavior (10-4). As before, we confine the discussion to $\mathrm{Re}\,\ell > -1/2$.

Having defined a continuation for the various factors in (10-20), Regge rewrote the partial-wave sum as an integral in the complex ℓ plane such that each term in the partial-wave summation is the residue of a pole in the contour integration:

---

*A related transformation was used by Poincaré and Nicholson[50] in 1910 in connection with the bending of electromagnetic waves by a sphere. The transformation was introduced in its present form by Watson[51] in 1918 and later resurrected by Sommerfeld.[52] The author is indebted to E. Guth for calling this early history to his attention.

$$A(q,z) = \frac{1}{q} \int_P d\ell\, (2\ell+1) \frac{(e^{2i\delta_\ell} - 1)}{4} \frac{P_\ell(-z)}{\sin \pi\ell} \quad . \tag{10-21}$$

Near the pole of the integrand at $\ell = n \geq 0$, we have

$$\frac{P_\ell(-z)}{\sin \pi\ell} \sim \frac{P_n(-z)}{\pi(\ell-n)\,(-1)^n} = \frac{P_n(z)}{\pi(\ell-n)} \tag{10-22}$$

so the residue comes out correctly. The contour P encloses all integers $\ell = 0$ to $\ell = N$, and the limit $N \to \infty$ is taken (Fig. 10-1).

Now it is of interest to study the limit $z \to \pm\infty$ at fixed q, which is equivalent to the limit of infinite momentum transfer t on account of the relation $t = -2q^2 (1-z)$. This limit takes us out of the physical region $1 \geq z \geq -1$. The motivation for studying it is twofold:

i) Large momentum transfers correspond to small distances. Only low partial waves, or states strongly influenced by an attractive potential, can penetrate the centrifugal barrier to small distances. So a study of large t is a study of the strongly scattered partial waves that can resonate or bind.

ii) Relativistically, there is another channel where t becomes the energy variable and the limit $t \to \infty$ has direct physical significance.

The original partial-wave expansion (10-20) is not useful for the study of $z \to \infty$ because it converges only at small z (inside an elliptical boundary discovered by Lehmann[47]). The difficulty is easily located in the behavior

$$P_\ell(z) \underset{z \to \infty}{\sim} z^{\ell_R + i\,\ell_I} \tag{10-23}$$

which holds for all complex ℓ with $\mathrm{Re}\,\ell \geq -1/2$, and makes the sum (10-20) or integral (10-21) over large real ℓ unmanageable as $z \to \infty$. Regge remedied this difficulty by shifting the contour from real ℓ to the axis $\ell = -1/2 + \epsilon + i\,\ell_I$ where (10-23) merely oscillates as ℓ grows large (Fig. 10-1). The new contour will therefore be useful provided the contributions from the semicircle at infinite ℓ, and from singularities isolated by the shift of contour, are sufficiently well behaved.

First, we discuss the singularities encountered in the shifts of contour. The factors $(2\ell+1)$ and $P_\ell(-z)$ have no singularities at any finite ℓ, and the only singularities of $\left[\sin \pi\ell\right]^{-1}$ are poles at integer ℓ, none of which are encountered in the shift. There remain the Regge pole singularities of $S = \exp(2i\delta_\ell)$. Regge found for a broad class of potentials, including the Yukawa potentials in which we are interested, that S has only poles at $\mathrm{Re}\,\ell > -1/2$. As we have seen, these lie above the real axis for $E > 0$.

The simplicity of singularities encountered in the shift of contour bodes well for the new representation, but the behavior at large ℓ must also be investigated. For superpositions of Yukawa potentials, the phase shifts at large ℓ should be small, and Regge studied them by an extension of the WKB method. After some rather difficult mathematics, he found that the number of poles to the right of any line $\mathrm{Re}\,\ell = N$

is finite, and the contribution from the semicircle at large ℓ vanishes for small z where the original expansion (10-21) was well-defined.*

Thus the representation can be written as a sum over poles plus the integral along $\mathrm{Re}\,\ell = -1/2 + \epsilon$:

$$A(q,z) = \frac{1}{q} \int_{-i\infty - \frac{1}{2} + \epsilon}^{+i\infty - \frac{1}{2} + \epsilon} d\ell\,(2\ell+1) \left(\frac{e^{2i\delta_\ell} - 1}{4} \right) \frac{P_\ell(-z)}{\sin \pi\ell}$$

$$+ \sum_i \frac{\beta_i(q)}{\sin \pi\, \alpha_i(q)} P_{\alpha_i(q)}(-z) \quad . \tag{10-24}$$

In the pole terms, the residue is written for convenience as a product of P_α, which contains all the angular dependence, and a factor β. The "Sommerfeld-Watson representation" (10-24) immediately allows the desired extension to large z, where in view of (10-23), the poles with $\ell_R > -1/2$ dominate the integral and the pole furthest to the right (labeled α_1) dominates all others:

$$A(q,z) \underset{z \to \infty}{\sim} \frac{\beta_1}{\sin \pi\, \alpha_1} z^{\alpha_1} \quad . \tag{10-25}$$

For potentials which are not superpositions of Yukawas, the semicircle at large ℓ generally does not vanish. An example which can be solved in closed form is provided by the square well potential.[53)] When

*Actually, Regge's original proof applied only to $|\ell| \to \infty$ along non-vertical rays. The necessary extension of the proof to the vertical ray $\mathrm{Re}\,\ell$ = constant, $|\mathrm{Im}\,\ell| \to \infty$, at $q^2 + i\epsilon$ has been made by F. Calogero, Nuovo Cimento 28, 701 (1963). H. Cheng (to be published) has extended this result to all q^2.

the semicircle fails to vanish, (10-24) and (10-25) do not hold. Thus, superpositions of Yukawa potentials have special properties at large z, which are of great importance for the Mandelstam representation (which cannot exist unless A is bounded by a finite power of z) and relativistic scattering (where (10-25) describes the high-energy behavior in a crossed channel).

Equation (10-24) has several limitations. First, Regge proved (10-24) under restrictions on the superposition of Yukawa potentials which imply a behavior less singular than $V \sim 1/r^2$ at the origin and more convergent than $V \sim \exp(-mr)$ at large r. Secondly, there is no fundamental reason why the integral has to follow the line $\mathrm{Re}\,\ell = -1/2$. Subsequent investigations by Froissart,[54] Mandelstam,[55] Newton,[56] and others showed that the boundary of integration can be pushed to the left of $\mathrm{Re}\,\ell = -1/2$ by any finite distance.

Is Regge's extension away from integer ℓ unique? Certainly not; for example, one could always make the change

$$e^{2i\delta_\ell} \rightarrow e^{2i\delta_\ell}(1 + \sin \pi\ell) \qquad (10\text{-}26)$$

without affecting the behavior in the physical limit of integer ℓ. It can be seen, however, that the new term in (10-26) is more divergent on the semicircle at large ℓ. Squires,[57] Prosperi,[58] Cheng and Nunez-Lagos,[59] and others have shown that Regge's extension is, in fact, unique if a representation of form (10-24) is to hold without additional contributions from the semicircle at large ℓ.

Before proceeding further, it may be helpful to review the standard methods[60] for extending P_ℓ to complex ℓ. The representation

$$P_\ell(z) = \frac{1}{2^\ell \, \ell!} \frac{d^\ell}{dz^\ell} (z^2 - 1)^\ell \qquad (10\text{-}27)$$

for integer ℓ can be expressed as a Cauchy integral around a contour C enclosing z (Schläfli representation):

$$P_\ell(z) = \frac{1}{2\pi i} \int_C \frac{dx}{x-z} \left[\frac{1}{2^\ell \, \ell!} \frac{d^\ell}{dx^\ell} (x^2 - 1)^\ell \right] . \qquad (10\text{-}28)$$

Integration by parts gives the form

$$P_\ell(z) = \frac{1}{2\pi i \, 2^\ell} \int_C \frac{(x^2 - 1)^\ell \, dx}{(x - z)^{\ell+1}} , \qquad (10\text{-}29)$$

which we extend to complex ℓ. Straightforward differentiation shows that (10-29) satisfies the usual differential equation

$$\frac{d}{dz} \left[(1 - z^2) \frac{dP_\ell}{dz} \right] + \ell(\ell+1) P_\ell = 0 \qquad (10\text{-}30)$$

at all ℓ. At non-integer ℓ, the integrand of (10-29) has branch points at $x = \pm 1$, $x = z$, and $x = \infty$ so the contour C must be specified more carefully now. Of the two independent solutions of the second order differential equation (10-30), the "Legendre function of the first kind" is given by the choice of contour in Fig. 10-2. With this choice, (10-29) satisfies

$$\begin{aligned} P_\ell(z = 1) &= 1 , \\ P_\ell(z) &= P_{-\ell-1}(z) , \end{aligned} \qquad (10\text{-}31)$$

and the usual recursion relations at all ℓ. It has a cut in z which can be taken from $z = -1$ to $-\infty$, and is analytic in ℓ.

An alternative representation was suggested by Laplace, who took for C a circle around z:

$$x = z + \sqrt{z^2 - 1}\; e^{i\phi} \quad . \tag{10-32}$$

Changing variables from x to ϕ, one finds

$$P_\ell(z) = \frac{1}{\pi} \int_0^\pi \left(z + \sqrt{z^2 - 1}\, \cos\phi\right)^\ell d\phi \quad . \tag{10-33}$$

At $\mathrm{Re}\, \ell > -1/2$ and large z, (10-33) easily yields the z^ℓ behavior we have already made use of.

To project a physical partial wave

$$A_\ell(q) = \frac{1}{2} \int_{-1}^{1} dz\, P_\ell(z)\, A(q,z) \tag{10-34}$$

out of the Sommerfeld-Watson representation (10-24), what is needed is the relation

$$\frac{1}{2} \int_{-1}^{1} dz\, P_\ell(z)\, P_\alpha(-z) = \frac{\sin \pi\alpha}{\pi\,(\alpha - \ell)(\alpha + \ell + 1)} \tag{10-35}$$

(ℓ is integer, α is complex). The reader can verify that (10-35) reduces to the usual relations $(-1)^\ell/(2\ell+1)$ as α approaches ℓ, and zero as α approaches a different integer.

Consider now the contribution from one Regge pole at α to A_ℓ:

$$\frac{\beta(q)}{\pi\,(\alpha(q) - \ell)(\alpha + \ell + 1)} \quad . \tag{10-36}$$

If α is close to ℓ, the small denominator gives a big contribution which can change rapidly with energy. In this region it is worthwhile to expand α in a Taylor series about E_ℓ, the energy where $\operatorname{Re}\alpha = \ell$ (assuming that there is such an energy):

$$\alpha \cong \ell + (E-E_\ell) \frac{d\,\alpha_R(E_\ell)}{dE} + i\,\alpha_I(E_\ell) \quad . \tag{10-37}$$

Substitution of (10-37) into (10-36) gives the Breit-Wigner form

$$\frac{\beta}{\pi(\alpha+\ell+1)\dfrac{d\,\alpha_R(E_\ell)}{dE}\left[E - E_\ell + i\dfrac{\Gamma}{2}\right]} \quad , \tag{10-38}$$

$$\frac{\Gamma}{2} = \frac{\alpha_I(E_\ell)}{d\,\alpha_R(E_\ell)/dE} \quad . \tag{10-39}$$

The resonance width Γ should vanish below threshold where there is no state to decay into. This is ensured by $\alpha_I = 0$ (10-10) and the condition (10-18), which prevents $d\alpha_R/dE$ from vanishing below threshold. Below threshold then, (10-38) exhibits a pole -- interpreted as a bound state -- at E_ℓ.

Regge[24)] has given an interesting interpretation to α_I. Just as Γ represents the width of the resonance in energy, α_I represents its width in angular momentum. The conjugate variable to energy is time, and the lifetime Δt of the resonance satisfies the relation $\Delta t \sim \hbar/\Gamma$. Similarly, the conjugate variable to angular momentum is angle, and the angle $\Delta\theta$ through which the particle orbits during the course of the resonance satisfies the relation $\Delta\Theta \sim h/\alpha_I$. For a resonance with long lifetime, α_I is small and $\Delta\Theta$ is large. For a bound state, Im α vanishes and the orbit becomes permanent.

If α is not close to ℓ, the contribution of (10-36) is likely to be smaller and to vary more slowly with energy. Therefore, far away poles and the integral at Re $\ell = -1/2$ do not normally produce resonances, and of course never produce bound states.

At threshold, it is well known that $\delta_\ell \sim q^{2\ell+1}$ for integer ℓ, so that $(\exp(2i\delta_\ell) - 1)$ has a branch point. It is not surprising, then, that both α and β have branch points involving $q^{2\alpha+1}$ or $q^{2\alpha}$ at threshold. The behavior of α, for example, can be shown[56,61] to be

$$\alpha(q^2) = \alpha(0) + a_1 q^2 + a_2 q^4 \; . \; . \; . \; . \; . \\ + b\,(e^{-i\pi} q^2)^{\alpha(0) + 1/2} \quad . \qquad (10\text{-}40)$$

For $\alpha(0) < 1/2$, the movement of α near threshold is controlled by b, which must be negative to ensure that $d\alpha_R/dE > 0$ below threshold and $\alpha_I > 0$ above threshold. The real part of α, being proportional to $b \cos \pi \left[\alpha(0) + 1/2\right]$, therefore starts to decrease above threshold when $\alpha(0)$ is negative and increases when $\alpha(0)$ is positive. For $\alpha(0) > 1/2$, the movement near threshold is controlled by a_1, which must be positive to ensure that $d\alpha_R/dE > 0$ below threshold. In this case, as for all $\alpha(0) > 0$, α_R continues to increase just above threshold.

Behavior further above threshold is more dependent on the particular potential used. If the potential is attractive at all r, but too weak to bind even the S-state $(\alpha(0) < 0)$, we know that there are no resonances, so α_R will normally continue the motion to the left that set in at threshold. If the potential is weakly attractive at small r and repulsive at large r, however, with $\alpha(0)$ still negative, the outer repulsive region may be capable of holding in a resonance, so α_R may swing back to the right after starting to the left above threshold. A typical behavior for a strongly attractive potential is illustrated in Fig. 10-3, where S- and P-wave bound states are followed by a D-wave resonance. At the resonance, note that $d\alpha_R/dE$ is positive so the resonance width (10-39) is positive as it must be. As the energy continues to increase and the phase shifts retreat to 0°, numerical calculations[62] show that the Regge pole moves back to the left. The imaginary part of α is now quite large; if it were not the one-pole formula (10-38) would hold again as α moves back to the left, but Γ would have the wrong sign (10-39).

From the point of view of phenomenology, if one sees experimentally several bound states and resonances with increasing ℓ, their positions can be used to estimate $d\alpha_R/dE$ and then their widths give α_I.

We have already remarked on the ordering of bound states and resonances for a particular Regge pole. There are certain exceptions to the ordering $E_S < E_P < E_D$ . . .:

i) In many nuclei, the ground state has a rather high spin. This can happen if β vanishes when α passes through the lower spin values, and Gell-Mann[63] has explored some of the mechanisms by which β can vanish.

ii) Above threshold, a complicated potential can lead to a complicated trajectory for α, so it is possible in principle to have different orderings.

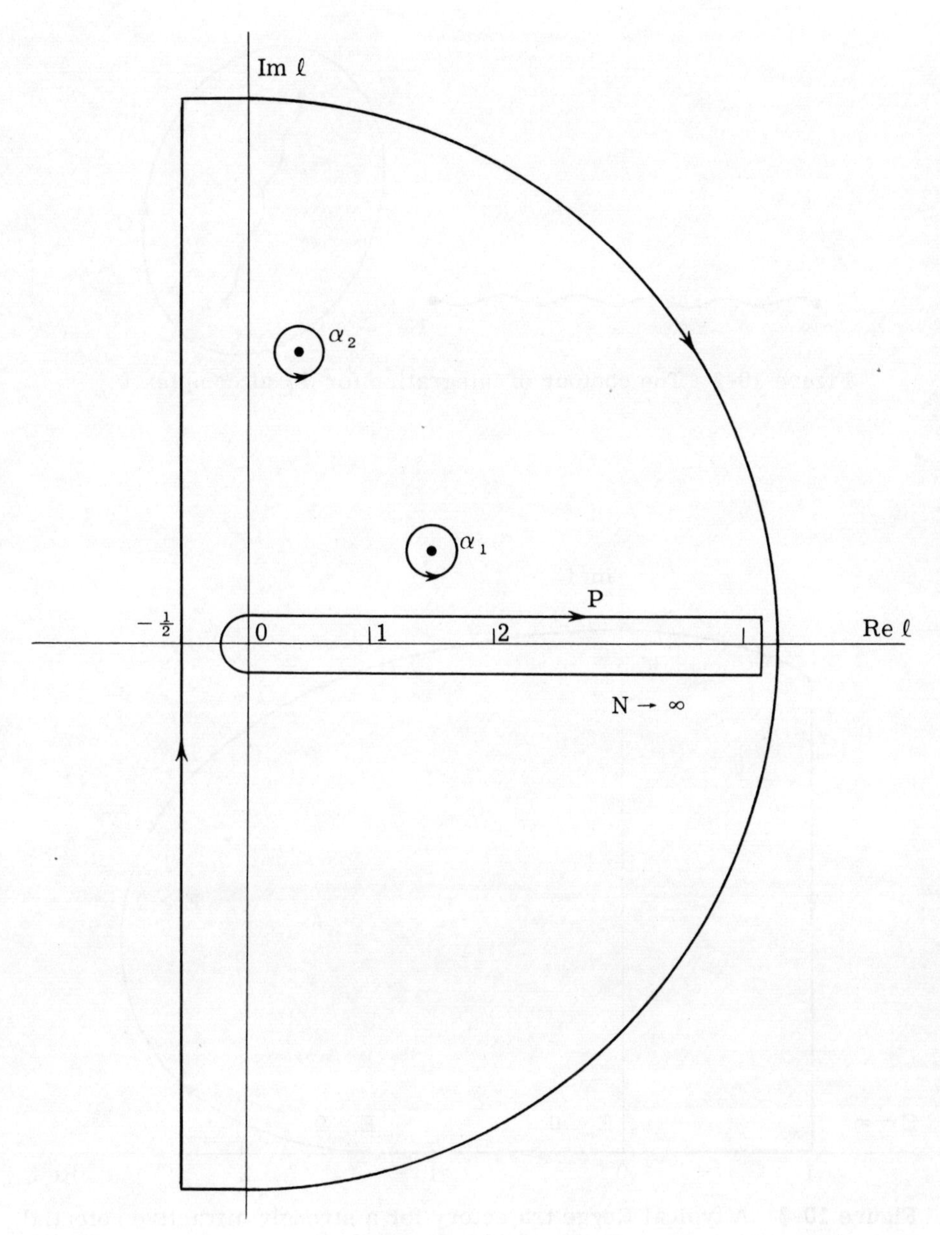

Figure 10-1 The contour of integration representing the scattering amplitude before (P) and after the shift from the real ℓ axis.

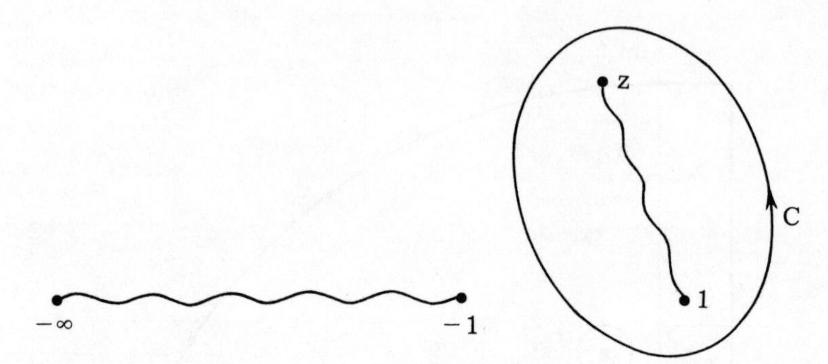

Figure 10-2 The contour of integration for P_ℓ at complex ℓ.

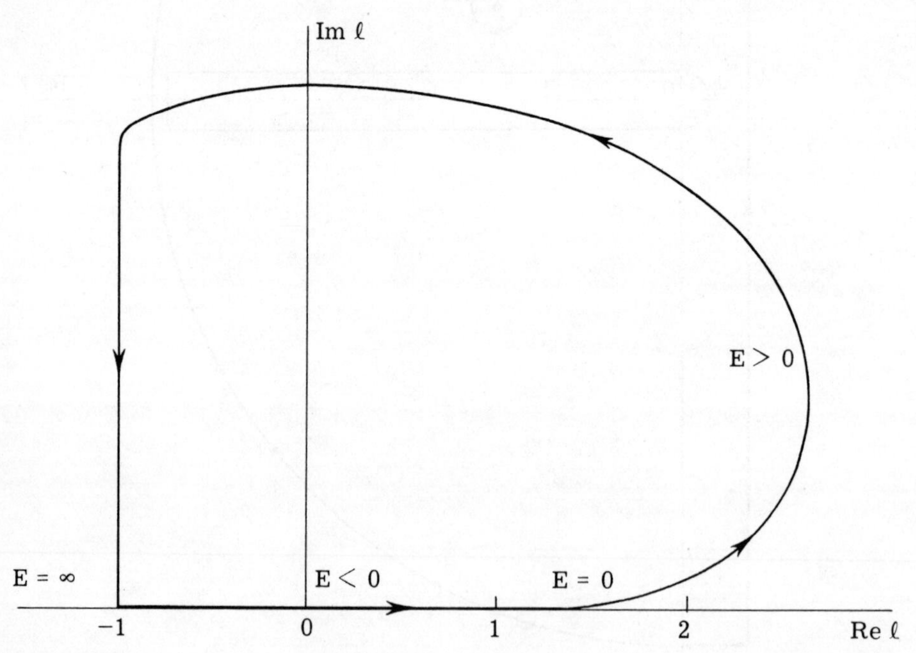

Figure 10-3 A typical Regge trajectory for a strongly attractive potential.

XI. REGGE POLES OF THE COULOMB SCATTERING AMPLITUDE*

Coulomb scattering is familiar and soluble in closed form. It therefore offers a unique opportunity to study the explicit, detailed behavior of Regge trajectories. The $1/r$ potential does, however, have certain special features which will be pointed out as we go along.

Consider the attractive Coulomb potential. The Schrödinger equation is

$$\nabla^2\psi + (E + \frac{e^2}{r})\,\psi = 0 \tag{11-1}$$

where $E = q^2$ is the kinetic energy, e^2 = the coupling constant of the Coulomb field, $\hbar = C = 2m = 1$. The ℓth partial wave satisfies the equation

$$\psi_\ell''(r) + (E + \frac{e^2}{r} - \frac{\ell(\ell+1)}{r^2})\,\psi_\ell(r) = 0 \quad . \tag{11-2}$$

As is well known, both these equations can be solved exactly. We consider first the partial-wave equation, taking the solution which behaves like

$$\psi_\ell(r) \sim r^{\ell+1} \tag{11-3}$$

at small r. The solution involves hypergeometric functions and can be found for arbitrary complex ℓ, though of course only integer $\ell = 0, 1, 2, \ldots$ give physical states.

---

*In this chapter, we follow closely the work of Singh.[64)]

A great simplification results from restricting our consideration to the asymptotic wave function, or more precisely to

$$S(E,\ell) = e^{2i\delta_\ell(E)} \quad . \tag{11-4}$$

The solution is then simply a ratio of gamma functions:

$$S(E,\ell) = \frac{\Gamma\left(\ell + 1 - \frac{ie^2}{2\sqrt{E}}\right)}{\Gamma\left(\ell + 1 + \frac{ie^2}{2\sqrt{E}}\right)} \quad . \tag{11-5}$$

The infinite part of the Coulomb phase,

$$\exp\left(\frac{ie^2}{2\sqrt{E}} \ \ell n\ r\right) \tag{11-6}$$

which is independent of angle and has no measurable effect, has been left out. It should also be noted that the form (11-5) is obtained from the wave equation for $E \geq 0$, $\ell > -1/2$ (where the wave function is normalizable) and then continued to $E < 0$, $\ell \leq -1/2$.

The function $\Gamma(z)$ has no zeroes in the entire z-plane. It has simple poles at $z = 0, -1, -2, \ldots$. Therefore, the only ℓ-plane singularities of $S(E,\ell)$ as given by (11-5) are poles of the gamma function in the numerator. These are the Regge poles. The position of the nth one is given by

$$\ell + 1 - \frac{ie^2}{2\sqrt{E}} = \alpha_n(E) + 1 - \frac{ie^2}{2\sqrt{E}} = -n \quad . \tag{11-7}$$

In other words, we have

$$\alpha_n(\epsilon) = -n + \alpha_o(E) \qquad (n = 0, 1, 2, \ldots) \tag{11-8}$$

where

$$\alpha_o(\epsilon) = -1 + \frac{ie^2}{2\sqrt{E}} \quad . \tag{11-9}$$

We can now trace the trajectories of the Regge poles in the ℓ-plane (Fig. 11-1) as we vary the energy along the real axis at negative energies $\sqrt{E} = i\,|\sqrt{E}|$ (this choice of sign puts us on the physical sheet, as discussed in Chapter II). When $E \to -\infty$, the nth Regge pole approaches $\ell = -n - 1$. As energy varies from $E = -\infty$ to $E = 0 - \epsilon$, all poles remain on the real ℓ axis and move in step with each other towards the point $\mathrm{Re}\,\ell = +\infty$, $\mathrm{Im}\,\ell = 0$. At the energies

$$E_{n,\ell} = \frac{e^4}{4(n + \ell + 1)^2} \tag{11-10}$$

the nth Regge pole crosses physical ℓ values ($\ell = 0, 1, 2, \ldots$). These are just the energies of the bound states in a Bohr atom. For positive energies, the nth Regge pole jumps to the straight line $\mathrm{Re}\,\ell = -n - 1$ and approaches $\ell = -n - 1$ as $E \to +\infty$.

It is also interesting to plot $\mathrm{Re}\,\ell$ against E for the various Regge poles (Fig. 11-2). The number of radial nodes in the wave functions associated with trajectories at $\ell = 0, 1, 2, \ldots$ is zero for the top trajectory, one for the next, and so forth. The trajectories with more radial nodes give bound states less readily because an increase in the number of radial nodes requires an increase in the radial kinetic energy $-d^2\psi/dr^2$.

The behavior of Regge poles for the infinite range Coulomb potential differs from that of the short-range potentials encountered in strong interaction theory in the following respects:

i) Neighboring poles are always separated by $\Delta\ell = 1$, leading to degeneracy of bound states with different ℓ but the same $n + \ell$ (11-10). This degeneracy is a special feature of the $1/r$ potential which does not hold in general.

ii) Short-range potentials cannot bind states of arbitrarily high angular momentum: the centrifugal barrier $\ell(\ell+1)/r^2$ dominates $\rho e^{-\mu r}/r$ at all r when ℓ is sufficiently large, unless $\mu = 0$. So the Regge trajectory does not normally proceed all the way to the right. Furthermore, it is normally continuous at threshold, instead of the jump exhibited by the Coulomb case.

A repulsive Coulomb potential is obtained by replacing e^2 with $-e^2$ in all the previous results. For example, the nth Regge pole is given by

$$\alpha_n(E) = -n - 1 - \frac{ie^2}{2\sqrt{E}} \quad . \tag{11-11}$$

There are still an infinite number of Regge poles, but they give no physical bound states (Fig. 11-1). Below threshold, the poles move to the left, and above threshold they have $\text{Im}\,\alpha < 0$, but as all this behavior occurs at $\mathrm{Re}\,\alpha < -1/2$, it does not violate the general properties established in the previous chapter for $\mathrm{Re}\,\alpha > -1/2$.

From the explicit formula for $\alpha_n(E)$, it is analytic in E with a branch point at $E = 0$ and cut along the positive real axis. It satisfies the dispersion relation

$$\mathrm{Re}\,\alpha_n(E) = \alpha_n(-\infty) + \frac{\mathrm{P.V.}}{\pi} \int_0^\infty \frac{\mathrm{Im}\,\alpha_n(E')\,dE'}{E' - E} \tag{11-12}$$

with

$$\alpha_n(-\infty) = -n-1 \quad ,$$

$$\mathrm{Im}\,\alpha_n(E) = \frac{e^2}{2\sqrt{E}} \quad , \tag{11-13}$$

as the reader can easily verify.

We turn now to the complete scattering amplitude, which depends on E and the momentum transfer $t = -2E(1 - \cos\Theta)$. It is the sum over physical partial waves:

$$A(E,t) = \frac{1}{\sqrt{E}} \sum_{\ell=0}^{\infty} (2\ell+1) \frac{[S(E,\ell) - 1]}{2i} P_\ell\left(1 + \frac{t}{2E}\right) \tag{11-14}$$

which can be rewritten in the Sommerfeld-Watson form discussed in the previous chapter. Alternatively, we make use of the special property of the Coulomb amplitude, that it can be put in the closed form

$$A(E,t) = \frac{\Gamma\left(1 - \frac{ie^2}{2\sqrt{E}}\right)}{\Gamma\left(\frac{ie^2}{2\sqrt{E}}\right)} \frac{i}{2\sqrt{E}} \left(\frac{-t}{4E}\right)^{-1 + \frac{ie^2}{2\sqrt{E}}}$$

$$= \frac{\Gamma(-\alpha_o(E))}{\Gamma(1 + \alpha_o(E))} \left(\frac{i}{2\sqrt{E}}\right) \left(\frac{-t}{4E}\right)^{\alpha_o(E)} \quad . \qquad (11\text{-}15)$$

It may be wondered how the sum over Regge poles can be compatible with the simple form (11-15). What happens is that the leading pole term can be expanded as $a\,t^{\alpha_o} + b\,t^{\alpha_o - 1} + \ldots$, and all but the leading power cancels with the other pole terms at $\alpha_o - 1$, $\alpha_o - 2$, ...

We note in passing that the energy and momentum transfer singularities of $A(E,t)$, as given by Eq. (11-15), provide an explicit illustration of the Mandelstam representation. The gamma function in the numerator gives the bound-state poles in the energy E, with the correct degeneracy. There is the usual cut in energy from $E = 0$ to $E = \infty$. In the t variable, there is a branch cut starting at $t = 0$, which we take to run over the real t-axis from 0 to $+\infty$. The explicit discontinuity

$$A_t(E,t) = \frac{1}{2i}\left[A(E, t + i\epsilon) - A(E, t - i\epsilon)\right] \qquad (11\text{-}16)$$

is given by

$$A_t(E,t) = \frac{i\pi}{2\sqrt{E}} \left(\frac{t}{4E}\right)^{\alpha_o(E)} \frac{\Theta(t)}{\left[\Gamma(1 + \alpha_o(E))\right]^2} \quad . \qquad (11\text{-}17)$$

Note that A_t has no bound-state poles in E, although A does. We can also find the double spectral function

$$\rho(E,t) = \frac{1}{2i}\left[A_t(E + i\epsilon, t) - A_t(E - i\epsilon, t)\right] \quad . \qquad (11\text{-}18)$$

It is

$$\rho(E,t) = \frac{i\pi}{4\sqrt{E}}\left[\frac{\left(\frac{t}{4E}\right)^{\alpha_o(E)}}{\left[\Gamma\,(1+\alpha_o(E))\right]^2} + \frac{\left(\frac{t}{4E}\right)^{\alpha_o^*(E)}}{\left[\Gamma\,(1+\alpha_o^*(E))\right]^2}\right] \quad . \qquad (11\text{-}19)$$

For positive energies A, A_t, and ρ have oscillations in the momentum transfer, with magnitude and period controlled by the real and imaginary parts of $\alpha_o(E)$ respectively. For negative energies A and A_t behave as t^{α_o} at large t, but α_o is now real.

Coulomb scattering of Klein-Gordan particles can also be solved exactly. With $\hbar = c = 1$ and the energy labelled as W, the equation is

$$\phi_\ell'' + \left[\left(W \pm \frac{e^2}{r}\right)^2 - m^2 - \frac{\ell(\ell+1)}{r^2}\right]\phi_\ell = 0 \quad . \qquad (11\text{-}20)$$

Collecting the $1/r^o$, $1/r$, and $1/r^2$ terms, we find that (11-20) has the same form as the Schrödinger equation (11-2) with the replacements E (non-relativistic kinetic energy) $\rightarrow W^2 - m^2$, $e^2/r \rightarrow 2\,W\,e^2/r$ (at threshold, 2W is 2m, which was taken equal to one in the Schrödinger equation), and $\ell(\ell+1)/r^2 \rightarrow (\ell(\ell+1) - e^4)/r^2$. Therefore, the S-matrix is

$$S(E,\ell) = \frac{\Gamma\,(\ell' - \ell_o(E))}{\Gamma\,(\ell' + 2 + \ell_o(E))} \qquad (11\text{-}21)$$

where

$$\ell' = \left[(\ell + \tfrac{1}{2})^2 - e^4\right]^{1/2} - \tfrac{1}{2} \quad , \qquad (11\text{-}22)$$

$$\ell_o(E) = -1 \pm \frac{e^2\,E}{(m^2 - E^2)^{1/2}} \quad . \qquad (11\text{-}23)$$

The behavior is in many ways similar to the non-relativistic case. A few of the differences are:

i) In addition to the channel which gives a cut from $E = m$ to $E = \infty$, there is a crossed channel giving a cut from $E = -m$ to $E = -\infty$. Kinematically, the Klein-Gordan equation represents a relativistic particle scattering from a fixed (infinite mass) source. In the crossed channel, we have the antiparticle scattering from the same fixed source, so naturally it behaves with the opposite sign of charge -- if the particle had bound states, the antiparticle has none, and vice versa. The crossing relations are unusually simple as a consequence of the infinite mass of the source.

ii) In addition to the Regge poles, the factor $\left[(\ell + \frac{1}{2})^2 - e^4\right]^{1/2}$ introduces a fixed branch cut in ℓ running from $\ell = -1/2 - e^2$ along the real ℓ axis to $\ell = -1/2 + e^2$. When $e^2 \geq 1/2$, this cut overtakes the physical state $\ell = 0$ and there is no consistent solution.

Singh has also solved the Coulomb scattering of Dirac particles with similar results. In this case, the physical states are at half-integer J, and at infinite energy the Regge poles are shifted by spin 1/2 to start near -1/2, -3/2, . . . rather than -1, -2, ...

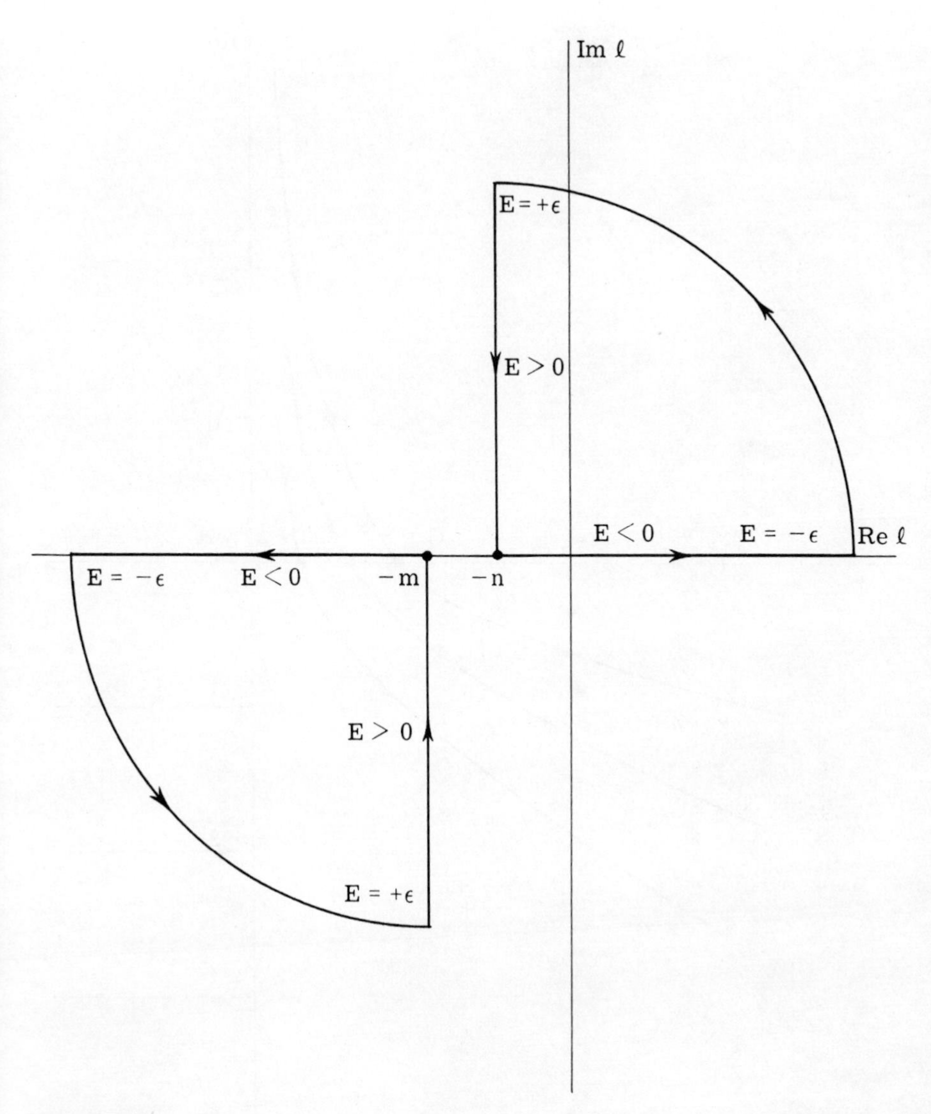

Figure 11-1 The effects of attractive and repulsive Coulomb potentials are illustrated by the Regge trajectories moving to the right from $-n$, and to the left from $-m$, respectively.

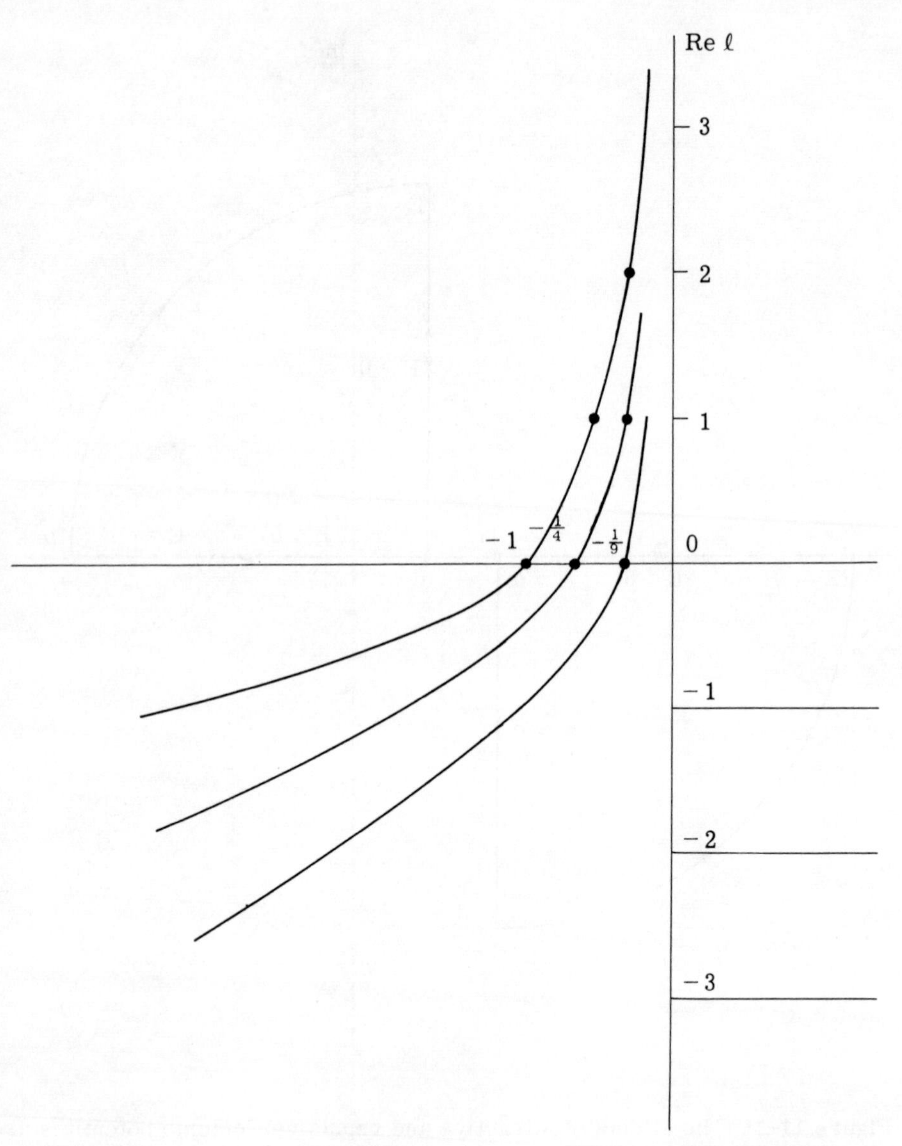

Figure 11-2 The variation of the real part of ℓ with energy (in units $e^4/4$) for the leading trajectories in an attractive Coulomb potential.

XII. MORE ABOUT REGGE POLES

In Coulomb scattering we were able to follow Regge poles explicitly into the region $\text{Re}\,\ell < -1/2$. It turned out that the nth Regge pole started from $\ell = -n-1$ at $E = -\infty$ and returned along the axis $\text{Re}\,\ell = -n-1$ as E approached $+\infty$ (Fig. 11-1).

Now consider a superposition of Yukawa potentials with finite mass exchange:

$$V(r) = -\frac{1}{2M^2} \int_{m_1^2}^{m_2^2} dm^2\, \rho(m^2)\, \frac{e^{-mr}}{r} \quad . \tag{12-1}$$

The scattering cannot be solved in closed form, but the Regge poles can be followed by numerical methods.[62] At small energies, the behavior is completely different from Coulomb scattering, with at most only a limited trajectories moving to the right of $\text{Re}\,\ell > -1/2$. But at large $|E|$, the Yukawa trajectories look more similar to Coulomb trajectories, and they both end at $\ell = -n-1$ in the limit $|E| \to \infty$ (Fig. 10-3). What is the cause of this similarity?

It is well known that as $E \to \infty$, the scattering amplitude for a Yukawa potential approaches the potential term. The potential term with finite mass exchange at large momentum transfers behaves like

$$\frac{1}{t-m^2} = \frac{1}{t} + \frac{m^2}{t^2} + \frac{m^4}{t^3} \cdots . \tag{12-2}$$

A Regge pole term at $\ell = \alpha$ behaves asymptotically like t^{α} (this was established in Chapter 10 for $\operatorname{Re}\alpha > -1/2$ and will be extended to $\operatorname{Re}\alpha < -1/2$ later in the present chapter). In the high-energy limit, then, (12-2) implies the existence of Regge poles at $\ell = -1, -2, \ldots$ The poles are there whatever the exchanged mass, except that in the Coulomb case ($m^2 = 0$), all but the t^{-1} contribution to the amplitude cancel (Eq. (11-15)).

The relation between Yukawa and Coulomb scattering at high energies is also evident in spatial coordinates. Large momentum transfers correspond to small r. At small r, both Yukawa and Coulomb potentials behave like $1/r$, so it is not surprising that the Regge trajectories approach the same limits.

Simple arguments also indicate what happens if a superposition of Yukawa potentials is less singular than $1/r$ at small distances. Consider a superposition of three Yukawas, represented by

$$V(r) = \frac{-1}{2M^2}\left[\frac{\rho_1 e^{-m_1 r}}{r} + \frac{\rho_2 e^{-m_2 r}}{r} + \frac{\rho_3 e^{-m_3 r}}{r}\right] \tag{12-3}$$

in ordinary space, or by

$$\frac{1}{\pi}\left[\frac{\rho_1}{m_1^2 - t} + \frac{\rho_2}{m_2^2 - t} + \frac{\rho_3}{m_3^2 - t}\right] \tag{12-4}$$

in the scattering amplitude. At large energies and momentum transfer, the amplitude normally behaves like t^{-1}, but if

$$\rho_1 + \rho_2 + \rho_3 = 0 \tag{12-5}$$

it becomes t^{-2} and if, in addition,

$$\rho_1 m_1^2 + \rho_2 m_2^2 + \rho_3 m_3^2 = 0 \tag{12-6}$$

then it becomes t^{-3}. Back in ordinary space, we find

$$V(r) = -\frac{1}{2M^2}\left[\frac{\rho_1 + \rho_2 + \rho_3}{r} - (\rho_1 m_1 + \rho_2 m_2 + \rho_3 m_3) + (\rho_1 m_1^2 + \rho_2 m_2^2 + \rho_3 m_3^2)\, r + \ldots\ldots\right] . \tag{12-7}$$

Thus, in the high-energy limit, the amplitude behaves like t^{-2} when the coefficient of $1/r$ vanishes (indicating there is no Regge pole at $\ell = -1$), behaves like t^{-3} when the coefficients of $1/r$ and r vanish (no Regge pole at $\ell = -1$ or $\ell = -2$), and is insensitive to the non-singular r^0 term in the potential.

Another interesting question concerns the behavior at $\ell = -1/2$. Consider the Schrödinger equation

$$\left[\frac{p_r^2}{2m} + \frac{\ell(\ell+1)}{2m\, r^2} + V\right]\psi = E\psi . \tag{12-8}$$

In a bound state $p_r \geq \hbar/2r$ (Heisenberg uncertainty principle). Therefore, we have

$$E \geq \frac{\hbar^2}{8mr^2} + \frac{\ell(\ell+1)}{2mr^2} + V . \tag{12-9}$$

For arbitrarily small attractive V, a bound state $E \leq 0$ is possible at $\ell = -1/2$, where $\ell(\ell+1) = -1/4$. Thus the first Regge pole gets as far as $\mathrm{Re}\,\ell = -1/2$ for an arbitrarily weak attraction.* Now if the potential has an attractive term a/r^2 $(a < 0)$, the operator

$$\frac{\hbar^2}{8mr^2} + \frac{\ell(\ell+1)}{2mr^2} + \frac{a}{r^2} \tag{12-10}$$

is attractive even for $\mathrm{Re}\,\ell$ somewhat larger than $-1/2$, in fact up to $\mathrm{Re}\,\ell = -1/2 + \sqrt{-a}$. An attractive $1/r^2$ potential is sufficiently singular to bind at any energy. Therefore, there is a singularity extending up to $\mathrm{Re}\,\ell = -1/2 + \sqrt{-a}$ at all energies.

<u>Example</u>: The Klein-Gordan equation is

$$\left[(E - V)^2 - p^2 - m^2\right] \phi = 0 \quad . \tag{12-11}$$

The "ordinary" potential term $-2\,EV$ is positive for attractive potential $(V < 0)$, so the V^2 term always represents an attractive effect. For example, if $V = \pm e^2/r$ then $V^2 = e^4/r^2$. In the exact solution of the Klein-Gordan equation with Coulomb forces (11-21), one indeed finds a fixed cut from $\mathrm{Re}\,\ell = -1/2 - e^2$ to $-1/2 + e^2$.

A convenient power series method for analyzing these and other properties of Regge poles in more detail has been developed by Mandelstam.[55] He considers a potential which can be expanded in powers of r:

---

*Actually, Gribov and Pomeranchuk,[65] and Wilson, have shown that an infinite number of poles converge on $\ell = -1/2$ at threshold for either an attractive or repulsive Yukawa potential (but not in the Coulomb limit).

$$V(r) = \sum_{n=0}^{\infty} v_n r^{n-1} \quad . \tag{12-12}$$

The radial wave function $\psi(r)$ is written

$$\psi(r) = \phi(r) e^{iqr} \quad . \tag{12-13}$$

Substituting (12-13) into the radial Schrödinger equation (10-2), one finds

$$\phi''(r) + 2iq\,\phi'(r) - \left[\frac{\ell(\ell+1)}{r^2} + \sum_{n=0}^{\infty} v_n r^{n-1}\right] \phi(r) = 0 \quad . \tag{12-14}$$

Setting

$$\phi(r) = \sum_{m=0}^{\infty} a_m r^{s+m} \tag{12-15}$$

we obtain the recurrence relation

$$\left\lfloor (s+m)(s+m-1) - \ell(\ell+1) \right\rfloor a_m + 2iq\,(s+m-1)\, a_{m-1}$$

$$- \sum_{n=0}^{\infty} v_n a_{m-1-n} = 0 \quad . \tag{12-16}$$

For $m = 0$, only the first term contributes, so that the factor multiplying $a_{m=0}$ must be zero. Accordingly, $s = \ell + 1$ or $-\ell$, i.e., as usual we have a "regular" and an "irregular" solution because of the invariance of the Schrödinger equation under the interchange $\ell \to -\ell - 1$. Whichever solution we start with, the higher terms follow explicitly from (12-16). Each term is explicitly an analytic function of ℓ in the whole plane. (The points ℓ = integer or half integer, where the coefficient of a_m can vanish, will require special discussion later.)

For a Yukawa potential v_n decreases with n like $(n!)^{-1}$, so at sufficiently large m, Eq. (12-16) allows one to find an M such that

$$\left|\frac{a_{m+1}}{a_m}\right| < \frac{M}{m} \tag{12-17}$$

in a given region of the ℓ-plane. Therefore, the power series converges for all ℓ and r, and the convergence is uniform with respect to ℓ. Thus, since the individual terms are analytic in the whole ℓ-plane, the same is true of the complete series. How, then, do singularities of the S-matrix in ℓ arise?

The solution for $s = \ell + 1$ (the "regular" solution) can be written

$$\psi(r) = e^{-iqr} - e^{-i\pi\ell}\; S(\ell,q)\; e^{iqr} \quad . \tag{12-18}$$

At a Regge pole, recall that $S = \infty$; the solution is purely "outgoing" for $q > 0$ or "decreasing exponential" for $q^2 < 0$, $q = i\,|q|$. So in

$$\phi(r) = e^{-2iqr} - e^{-i\pi\ell}\; S(\ell,q) \tag{12-19}$$

we look for ℓ such that the exponential e^{-2iqr} fails to develop.

The Coulomb case

$$V(r) = -\frac{e^2}{r} \tag{12-20}$$

is especially simple. Here, (12-16) for $s = \ell + 1$ reduces to

$$m\left[m + 2\ell + 1\right] a_m + \left[2iq\,(m+\ell) + e^2\right] a_{m-1} = 0 \quad . \tag{12-21}$$

For most ℓ,

$$a_m = -\frac{2iq}{m} a_{m-1} + \ldots . \qquad (12\text{-}22)$$

and the exponential $\Sigma\,(m!)^{-1}\,(-2iq)^m = \exp(-2iq)$ is built up. But for

$$\ell = -m - \frac{e^2}{2iq} \qquad m = 1, 2, \ldots \qquad (12\text{-}23)$$

the series terminals at a_{m-1} and the exponential cannot develop. This result agrees with the Coulomb trajectories derived in Chapter 11.

For the Yukawa case, where there are an infinite number of non-vanishing v_n, a solution in closed form is not available. The limit $|q| \to \infty$ can still be treated, however. The equation for $s = \ell + 1$ is

$$m\left[m + 2\ell + 1\right] a_m + \left[2iq\,(m+\ell) - v_o\right] a_{m-1} - \sum_{n=1}^{\infty} v_n\, a_{m-1-n} = 0 \quad . \qquad (12\text{-}24)$$

The exponential builds up in the usual way except at

$$\ell = -m + \frac{v_o}{2iq} \quad , \qquad m = 1, 2, 3, \ldots . \qquad (12\text{-}25)$$

Consider, for example, $\ell = -1 + v_o/2iq$. Taking $a_o = 1$, we find

$$a_1 = 0 \quad ,$$

$$a_2 = \frac{v_1}{2\,(1 + v_o/iq)} \quad ,$$

$$a_3 \sim -\frac{2iq}{3} a_2 \quad ,$$

$$a_m \sim -\frac{2iq}{m} a_{m-1} \quad . \qquad (12\text{-}26)$$

The leading powers in q sum up to $\sim q^{-2} \exp(-2iqr)$ which vanishes at large q. So $\ell = -1$ is the limiting position of a Regge pole as $q \to \pm\infty$, in agreement with our previous results.

Exercise: Prove that $\ell = -n$, $n = 2, 3, 4, \ldots$ are limiting positions of Regge poles as $q \to \pm\infty$.

Exercise: Prove that if $v_0 = 0$ (no 1/r term in the potential), there is no Regge pole at $\ell = -1$ as $q \to \pm\infty$.

Now let us return to the discussion following (12-16) and plug up a loophole which occurred there. At negative integral or half-integral ℓ, the solution which behaves at the origin like $r^{\ell+1}$ no longer exists. The coefficient of a_m in (12-16) becomes zero for $m = 2|\ell| - 1$ in these cases so that, if we attempted to construct the power series solution starting with $r^{\ell+1}$, the coefficients would be infinite from $a_{2|\ell|-1}$ upward. In defining our power series solution, we must therefore multiply the whole series by a factor which is zero at negative integral and half-integral values of $\ell < -1/2$: for instance, by

$$\frac{1}{\Gamma(\ell + 1)\,\Gamma(\ell + \frac{3}{2})} \quad . \tag{12-27}$$

This would affect neither the value of the scattering amplitude nor the analytic properties of ϕ. For ℓ a negative integer or half-integer, all the coefficients up through $a_{2|\ell|-2}$ would be zero, and those from $a_{2|\ell|-1}$ upwards would be finite. In other words, the wave function is the same as at the corresponding positive value of ℓ. In view of the relation (12-18) between the wave function and the S-matrix, we find:

$$S(q,\ell) = - e^{2i\pi\ell} \; S(q, -\ell-1) \qquad \ell = 0, 1/2, 1, \ldots \qquad (12\text{-}28)$$

The argument leading up to (12-28) must be re-examined when the sum of the first $2|\ell| - 2$ terms in (12-16) is zero so that $a_{2|\ell|-1}$, instead of being infinite, is undetermined. From our previous discussions, we know that a Regge pole is present when the sum of the first $2|\ell| - 2$ terms in (12-16) is zero. However, in the limit where the Regge pole reaches integer or half-integer ℓ, the coefficient of $a_{2|\ell|-1}$ also vanishes so the series does not terminate and the exponential can develop. This event, occurring at a unique ℓ on the Regge trajectory, means that the residue of the pole approaches zero as ℓ approaches the integer or half-integer value. In this case, (12-28) does not necessarily hold. Still another possibility is that Regge poles pass simultaneously through both ℓ and $2|\ell| - 1$. These properties, suggested by Mandelstam for integer and half-integer ℓ, can all be verified explicitly in the Coulomb case.[64)]

Besides the potentials considered by Mandelstam, another case which can be treated by a simple extension of his method is

$$V(x) = \sum_{n=-1}^{\infty} v_n \, r^{n-1} = v_{-1} \, r^{-2} + v_0 \, r^{-1} + \ldots . \qquad (12\text{-}29)$$

The equation for a_m (12-26) becomes

$$\left[(s+m)(s+m-1) - \ell(\ell+1) - v_{-1}\right] a_m + \left[2iq\,(s+m-1) - v_o\right] a_{m-1}$$

$$- \sum_{n=1}^{\infty} v_n\, a_{m-1-n} = 0 \quad . \tag{12-30}$$

As usual, the coefficient of a_o must vanish, giving

$$s = \frac{1}{2} \pm \sqrt{\left(\ell + \frac{1}{2}\right)^2 + v_{-1}} \quad . \tag{12-31}$$

The solution ϕ thus starts off as

$$r^{\frac{1}{2} \pm \sqrt{\left(\ell + \frac{1}{2}\right)^2 + v_{-1}}} \quad , \tag{12-32}$$

which has branch points at the zeroes of the square root, i.e., at

$$\ell = -\frac{1}{2} \pm \sqrt{-v_{-1}} \quad . \tag{12-33}$$

So just as the behavior in ℓ becomes less singular when the potential is less singular at small r, the behavior in ℓ becomes more singular as the potential becomes more singular at small r.

If $v_{-1} < 0$ (attraction), the singularities give a cut running along the real ℓ-axis from $\ell = -\frac{1}{2} - \sqrt{|v_{-1}|}$ to $\ell = -\frac{1}{2} + \sqrt{|v_{-1}|}$. This is what happened for the Klein-Gordan equation with Coulomb potential. On the other hand, if $v_{-1} > 0$ (repulsion), there is a cut on the line $\mathrm{Re}\,\ell = -\frac{1}{2}$ connecting $\ell = -\frac{1}{2} \pm \sqrt{|v_{-1}|}\ i$.

Exercise: Find the Regge poles for

$$V = \frac{v_{-1}}{r^2} + \frac{v_o}{r} \quad . \tag{12-34}$$

Potentials with a short-range repulsion more singular than $1/r^2$ have been considered by Limić[66] and by Regge and Predazzi.[67] For these potentials, the wave function at small r is no longer sensitive to the centrifugal barrier, and the boundary condition is independent of ℓ. Since the Schrödinger equation depends on ℓ only through the combination $\ell(\ell+1)$, the solution is now invariant under $\ell \to -\ell - 1$ and the symmetry relation (12-28) holds at all ℓ. If a short-range repulsion is combined with a long-range attraction (as in the usual picture of nuclear forces), the attraction controls bound states and resonances, and generally the movement of poles to $\text{Re}\,\ell > -1/2$ proceeds as usual, whereas the results of Limić, Regge, and Predazzi show that the behavior at $\text{Re}\,\ell < -1/2$ is extremely sensitive to how singular the repulsion is.

In addition to his studies of individual Regge poles to the left of $\text{Re}\,\ell = -1/2$, Mandelstam has shown how to extend the line integral in the Sommerfeld-Watson representation to the left. We have previously written the representation in the form

$$A(q,z) = -\frac{1}{2i} \int_{-\frac{1}{2} - i\infty}^{-\frac{1}{2} + i\infty} d\ell\,(2\ell+1)\,A(q,\ell)\,\frac{P_\ell(-z)}{\sin \pi\ell}$$

$$+ \sum_{\text{Re}\,\alpha_i > -\frac{1}{2}} (2\alpha_i + 1)\,a(q, \alpha_i)\,\frac{P_{\alpha_i}(-z)}{\sin \pi\alpha_i} \tag{12-35}$$

where α_i represents the position of a pole of S in the ℓ-plane, and $a(q, \alpha_i)$ the residue at the pole. Since $P_\ell(-z)$ behaves like $(-z)^\ell$ at infinity, the integral tends to zero faster than any pole at large z.

Now let us suppose, as is normally the case, that $A(q,\ell)$ can be extended to the left of $\mathrm{Re}\,\ell = -1/2$. We cannot simply move the integration contour in (12-35) to the left, since for $\mathrm{Re}\,\ell < -1/2$, $P_\ell(-z) = P_{-\ell-1}(-z)$ behaves like $z^{-\ell-1}$ at infinity and the asymptotic behavior of the integral would begin to grow again. Mandelstam therefore modified (12-35) by using the Legendre functions of the second kind, $Q_\ell(-z)$. These functions are analytic in the z-plane except for a cut running from -1 to ∞. They satisfy the identity

$$\frac{P_\ell(z)}{\sin \pi\ell} - \frac{Q_\ell(z)}{\pi \cos \pi\ell} = -\frac{Q_{-\ell-1}(z)}{\pi \cos \pi\ell} \quad . \tag{12-36}$$

At large z, Q_ℓ behaves like $z^{-\ell-1}$ for <u>all</u> ℓ.

The fact that both sides of (12-36) behave like z^ℓ for ℓ positive or negative led Mandelstam to write

$$\begin{aligned} A(q,z) &= \sum_{n=0}^{\infty} (2n+1)\, A(q,n)\, P_n(z) \\ &= \sum_{n=0}^{\infty} (2n+1)\, A(q,n)\, P_n(z) + \frac{1}{\pi} \sum_{n=1}^{\infty} (-1)^{n-1}\, 2n\, A(q, n - \tfrac{1}{2})\, Q_{n-\frac{1}{2}}(z) \\ &\quad - \frac{1}{\pi} \sum_{n=1}^{\infty} (-1)^{n-1}\, 2n\, A(q, n - \tfrac{1}{2})\, Q_{n-\frac{1}{2}}(z) \quad . \end{aligned} \tag{12-37}$$

He then transformed the first two sums into an integral of the Regge type, with $P_\ell(-z)/\sin \pi\ell$ replaced by

$$\frac{P_\ell(-z)}{\sin \pi\ell} - \frac{Q_\ell(-z)}{\pi \cos \pi\ell} \quad . \tag{12-38}$$

The contour was then deformed in the usual way to give

$$A(q,z) = -\frac{1}{2i} \int_{-\frac{1}{2} - i\infty}^{-\frac{1}{2} + i\infty} d\ell \, (2\ell+1) \, A(q,\ell) \left[\frac{P_\ell(-z)}{\sin \pi\ell} - \frac{Q_\ell(-z)}{\pi \cos \pi\ell}\right]$$

$$- \frac{1}{\pi} \sum_{n=1}^{\infty} (-1)^{n-1} \, 2n \, A(q, n - \tfrac{1}{2}) \, Q_{n-\frac{1}{2}}(z)$$

$$+ \sum_{\mathrm{Re}\,\alpha_i > -1/2} (2\alpha_i + 1) \, a(q,\alpha_i) \left[\frac{P_{\alpha_i}(-z)}{\sin \pi\alpha_i} - \frac{Q_{\alpha_i}(-z)}{\pi \cos \pi\alpha_i}\right] \quad . \tag{12-39}$$

As the function within brackets behaves like z^ℓ for all ℓ, it is now worthwhile to move the integration contour to the left. In doing so, we obtain contributions from the poles of $A(q,\ell)$ which are crossed, so the summation in the last term of (12-39) must be extended to include such poles. In addition to the Regge poles, the factor within brackets gives poles at $\ell = -n - \frac{1}{2}$ according to (12-36), and the associated residues are

$$\frac{1}{\pi^2} (-1)^{n-1} \, Q_{n-\frac{1}{2}}(z) \quad . \tag{12-40}$$

These poles will therefore give contributions to A(q,z) of the form

$$\frac{1}{\pi} (-1)^{n-1} 2n A(q, -n-\tfrac{1}{2}) Q_{n-\frac{1}{2}}(z) \quad . \tag{12-41}$$

According to the equality (12-28), these contributions will just cancel corresponding terms in the first summation of (12-39). If, therefore, we move the contour to Re $(\ell) = -L$, where $-N-\frac{1}{2} < -L < -N+\frac{1}{2}$ (N integral), the formula becomes

$$A(q,z) = -\frac{1}{2i} \int_{-L-i\infty}^{-L+i\infty} d\ell\,(2\ell+1)\,A(q,\ell) \left\{-\frac{Q_{-\ell-1}(-z)}{\pi \cos \pi\ell}\right\}$$

$$-\frac{1}{\pi} \sum_{n=N}^{\infty} (-1)^{n-1} 2n A(q, n-\tfrac{1}{2}) Q_{n-\frac{1}{2}}(z)$$

$$+ \sum_{\mathrm{Re}\,\alpha_i > -L} (2\alpha_i + 1)\, a(q,\alpha_i) \left\{\frac{-Q_{-\alpha_i-1}(-z)}{\pi \cos \pi\alpha_i}\right\} \quad . \tag{12-42}$$

The pole terms in the last summation behave as z^{α_i} at large z for each α_i, while the "background" term, represented by the integral and the first summation, goes down at least as fast as $z^{-\ell}$.

The factor $(\cos \pi\alpha_i)^{-1}$ in the Regge pole terms becomes infinite at half-integer values of ℓ. We have seen, following (12-28), that the residue associated with the Regge pole normally vanishes at negative half-integer, so the contribution to A(q,z) remains finite. Another possibility is for two Regge poles to pass simultaneously through half-integer values ℓ_0 and $-\ell_0 - 1$. From (12-36), it follows that

$$Q_{\ell_0}(z) = Q_{-\ell_0-1}(z) \qquad \ell_0 = 1/2, 3/2, \ldots, \tag{12-43}$$

so the contribution to $A(q,z)$ remains finite if the residues are the same. The Regge pole terms also become infinite at $\alpha = 0, 1, \ldots,$ where $Q_{-\alpha-1}$ has poles. This is the way physical bound states appear in (12-42). The reader can find examples of all these possibilities in Coulomb scattering.

XIII. REGGE POLES IN RELATIVISTIC SCATTERING

We have discussed non-relativistic scattering and found that Regge poles put many familiar facts in a different light, but without predicting any novel experimental results or any departure from established theory. Turning to relativistic theory, we know it must have a low-energy limit in which Regge poles appear, and even at higher energies a strong analogy **between** relativistic and non-relativistic potential scattering has been established (Chapter 6). This motivates us to conjecture that Regge poles also appear in relativistic scattering. It is this conjecture, combined with crossing relations,* which leads to really new results.**

---

* Readers who have followed only the material on Regge poles are advised to study the kinematics of crossing (Chapter 5, up through Eq. (5-15)) before proceeding to the applications of Regge poles to relativistic scattering.

** It was Mandelstam who first urged, in private discussions, the importance of Regge poles for high-energy scattering. Theoretical arguments for their occurrence were presented by Chew, Frautschi, and Mandelstam,[68)] by Gribov,[69)] and by Blankenbecler and Goldberger.[70)] Some of the early applications were made by Lovelace,[71)] Chew and Frautschi[5,72)] (for a summary, see Chew's speech[73)]), Gell-Mann and Zachariasen,[74)] Udgaonkar,[75)] Gribov and Pomeranchuk,[76,77)] and Domokos.[78)]

Non-relativistically, we considered only one channel, which we may take to be the channel where s is the energy variable and t is a momentum transfer variable. The Sommerfeld-Watson representation was dominated by one term at very large z (equivalently, at large t), and this term went like

$$g(s) \quad t^{\alpha(s)} \quad . \tag{13-1}$$

In the relativistic case, on account of crossing the same matrix element describes scattering in the channel where t is the energy variable and s is a momentum transfer. Here, large t means high energy, so (13-1) provides the leading term at high energies. Other Regge terms provide lower powers of energy. The leading terms can be compared directly with high-energy experiments. Another new feature is that unitarity must be satisfied in <u>both</u> channels, which puts new restrictions on the α's.

The description of applications to experiment will be left to later chapters. In the present chapter, we treat some theoretical matters: how partial-wave amplitudes are extended to complex ℓ without benefit of the Schrödinger equation, some of their properties, and how Regge poles shed light on the relativistic divergence problem. All these questions are undergoing rapid development and we can only give a brief introduction.

To define relativistic partial-wave amplitudes, we begin with the fixed-energy dispersion relation

$$A(z,s) = \frac{1}{\pi} \int^{\infty} \frac{A_z(z',s)\, dz'}{z' - z} \tag{13-2}$$

(the cut in t at fixed s is equivalent to a cut in z). The external particles are taken spinless for simplicity.* For integer ℓ, one defines

$$A_\ell(s) = \frac{1}{2} \int_{-1}^{1} P_\ell(z)\, dz\, \frac{1}{\pi} \int^{\infty} \frac{A_z(z',s)\, dz'}{z' - z} \qquad (13\text{-}3)$$

which is equivalent to

$$A_\ell(s) = \frac{1}{\pi} \int^{\infty} Q_\ell(z')\, A_z(z',s)\, dz' \quad . \qquad (13\text{-}4)$$

It is natural to extend A_ℓ to complex ℓ by means of these expressions, but at non-integral ℓ they differ. Which extension is more useful?

Let $\ell \to \infty$ along a ray in the right-half ℓ-plane, while z remains fixed. The behavior of Q_ℓ in this limit is more convergent with the result that (13-4) allows a Sommerfeld-Watson representation whereas (13-3) does not.** Because of the uniqueness of the continuation which allows the Sommerfeld-Watson representation, the continuation in terms of Q_ℓ is identical with Regge's continuation when the Schrödinger equation holds. For these reasons, one uses (13-4).

---

* For treatments of spin, see References 74 and 77, and contributions by Gell-Mann and Gribov to the Proceedings of the 1962 International Conference on High-Energy Physics at CERN.

**The usefulness of the extension (13-4) was first pointed out by M. Froissart in an unpublished speech at the La Jolla Conference on Strong and Weak Interactions (1961). It has independently been discussed by Gribov,[69] Squires,[57] Domokos,[78] Martin,[79] Omnès,[80] and others.

The asymptotic behavior of Q_ℓ is also of interest in connection with exchange potentials.[57,79] In the presence of exchange forces (13-4) becomes

$$A_\ell = \frac{1}{\pi}\left[\int_{z_o}^{\infty} Q_\ell(z')\, A_z^{dir}(z',s)\, dz' + \int_{-\infty}^{-z_o} Q_\ell(z')\, A_z^{ex}(z',s)\, dz'\right] . \qquad (13\text{-}5)$$

The first term is well-behaved at large ℓ, as before, but the second term has a bad behavior as $|\ell| \to \infty$ along the imaginary axis since

$$Q_\ell(z\, e^{\pm i\pi}) = - e^{\pm i\pi\ell}\, Q_\ell(z) . \qquad (13\text{-}6)$$

We must therefore form two amplitudes

$$A_\ell^{\pm} \equiv \frac{1}{\pi}\int_{z_o}^{\infty} dz'\, Q_\ell(z')\, (A_z^{dir}(z') \pm A_z^{ex}(-z')) \qquad (13\text{-}7)$$

both of which have good behavior as $|\ell| \to \infty$. The $\pm$ label is often called the "signature". Evidently

$$A_\ell^{+} = A_\ell \qquad \ell = 0, 2, \ldots ,$$

$$A_\ell^{-} = A_\ell \qquad \ell = 1, 3, \ldots . \qquad (13\text{-}8)$$

We further define

$$A^{\pm}(z) \equiv \sum_{\ell=0}^{\infty} (2\ell+1)\, A_\ell^{\pm}\, P_\ell(z) \qquad (13\text{-}9)$$

and perform the Sommerfeld-Watson transformation on each of these amplitudes separately. The complete physical amplitude is

$$A(z) = \frac{1}{2}\left[A^+(z) + A^+(-z) + A^-(z) - A^-(-z)\right] \tag{13-10}$$

so A^+ contributes only to even, A^- to odd, physical states.

The even and odd amplitudes have different Regge poles -- they would become the same only if the exchange potential went to zero.[74] It is not surprising that even and odd amplitudes must be treated separately. After all, the exchange potential creates the possibility that the potential is attractive for (say) even waves, repulsive for odd waves, and it would not make physical sense to require that a Regge pole must always cause a bound state in $\ell = 1$ before it could bind the $\ell = 2$ state. So in the presence of exchange potentials, a Regge trajectory produces a physical bound state or resonance every time it increases by two units, not one. This is a very general result which continues to hold even in the presence of spin, parity violation, etc.

Now suppose $A(z) \sim z^{\alpha}$ at large z with s fixed. On account of the property $Q_\ell(z) \sim z^{-\ell-1}$, we find that (13-4) and (13-7) converge if $\text{Re}\ \ell > \text{Re}\ \alpha$. So we can define A_ℓ for all $\text{Re}\ \ell > \text{Re}\ \alpha$ by using the Mandelstam representation.

How can we continue further? One method that has been used starts by continuing the elastic unitarity relation to arbitrary ℓ, where it becomes

$$\frac{A(\ell) - A^\dagger(\ell^*)}{2i} = q\, A^\dagger(\ell^*)\, A(\ell) \tag{13-11}$$

(i.e., the functional dependence is conjugated, but not ℓ itself). Equation (13-11) follows from the definition (13-4) of $A(\ell)$, either by use of analogues for the addition theorem reducing the product of two Legendre polynomials to one,[69,78,80] or by noting that there is a uniqueness theorem for functions defined at integer ℓ and suitably bounded as $|\ell| \to \infty$ in the right-half ℓ-plane, and that (13-11) satisfies the conditions of the theorem.[57,79] Equation (13-11) has led M. Goldberger to formulate the principle, "Unitarity loves the complex ℓ-plane". The reader can easily verify the principle for the S-matrix in Coulomb scattering,[64] Eq. (11-5) (i.e., $S^{\dagger}(\ell^*)\, S(\ell) = 1$).

The generalized unitarity condition (13-11), together with the Mandelstam representation, allow one to set up an N/D equation for arbitrary ℓ. Bardakci,[81] and Barut and Zwanziger,[61] used these conditions to show that the only singularities permitted at $\mathrm{Re}\, J > 1$ are Regge poles. The limitation to $\mathrm{Re}\, J > 1$ has to do with the possibility of elementary particles, which are not Regge poles but remain at fixed $J = 0$, $1/2$, or 1. In any case, the proofs of Regge poles are incomplete, since they are based on the elastic unitarity condition rather than full unitarity.

Another method for establishing the existence of Regge poles has been followed by Lee and Sawyer,[82] and by Amati, Fubini, Stanghellini, and collaborators.[83] They showed explicitly that Regge poles appear in the sum over an infinite set of ladder diagrams. Their work also ignored many-particle intermediate states in the unitarity condition, however.

Let us now turn to the divergence problem. The status of this problem in relativistic S-matrix theory was described in Chapter 9. Froissart showed that subtraction terms which are independent of the double spectral function cannot be permitted to grow faster than linearly in s, t, or u. This limited elementary particles to $J \leq 1$ as in conventional renormalization theory. The problem then arose, that bound states and resonances seem to require independent subtraction terms, but such terms would violate Froissart's limit if $J > 1$. On the other hand, resonances and bound states are associated with "spread-out wave functions", which might prevent the relativistic divergences from occurring at small distances if an adequate technical description of the spreading-out could be found. This led us to study Regge poles, which describe bound states and resonances in non-relativistic potential scattering. Now we are conjecturing that Regge poles also appear in relativistic theory, and we wish to show how they alleviate the divergence problem.[68)*]

According to the Regge pole conjecture, the amplitude at a given s can be represented by a sum of poles:

$$\sum_i \frac{\beta_i}{\sin \pi\alpha_i} P_{\alpha_i}(-z) \tag{13-12}$$

*Divergences are still by no means fully eliminated, however, because of our incomplete understanding of inelastic contributions.[68)] plus an integral which vanishes at large z. Alternatively, it can be represented by a Cauchy integral:

$$\frac{1}{\pi} \int^{\infty} \frac{dz' \, A_z(z',s)}{z' - z} \quad . \tag{13-13}$$

The connection between the two representations has to do with the fact[60] that $P_\alpha(-z)$ is an analytic function in the z-plane cut along the positive real axis from $z = 1$ to ∞, and that the discontinuity across the cut at arbitrary α is $-2i \sin \pi\alpha \, P_\alpha(z)$. Thus for $\mathrm{Re}\,\alpha < 0$, we may write the dispersion relation

$$P_\alpha(-z) = -\frac{\sin \pi\alpha}{\pi} \int_1^{\infty} \frac{dz' \, P_\alpha(z')}{z' - z} \tag{13-14}$$

for each Regge pole. In the sum over Regge poles plus background integral, the discontinuity over a finite strip from $z = 1$ to the beginning of the cut in (13-13) must vanish.

When there are Regge poles with $\alpha_i > 0$, A_z behaves asymptotically like z^α, which seems to necessitate subtractions in the Cauchy integral. In fact, this is just the reason why bound or resonant states appear to need subtractions like those for an elementary particle. However, the representation (13-12), and the left-side of (13-14), are perfectly well-defined at $\mathrm{Re}\,\alpha \geq 0$ and provide the necessary analytic continuation above $\mathrm{Re}\,\alpha = 0$. Thus, one can separate out any pole terms with $\mathrm{Re}\,\alpha \geq 0$ and continue them in their Regge form, and the remaining contributions to the dispersion relations in $\cos\Theta$ (or, equivalently, momentum transfer) will converge without subtraction. Individual physical partial waves need not be separated. An alternative, but equivalent, statement is to say that (13-14) requires subtractions when Re $\alpha \geq 0$, but the subtractions are not arbitrary, being determined by analytic continuation. Of course, since the form of a Regge pole term is known explicitly, we are never required to express it as a Cauchy integral, but we have been eager here to exhibit the relation with dispersion theory.

Now that bound states and resonances do not require independent subtraction terms, there is no problem with the Froissart limit. At large s and fixed negative t (where s is the energy variable and t represents momentum transfer), Froissart states that the amplitude cannot grow faster than linearly in s. Therefore, the Regge trajectories in the t-channel must have $\alpha(t) \leq 1$ at $t \leq 0$. But as t increases to positive values where it has the significance of energy variables in a second channel, $\alpha(t)$ can increase and cause bound states and resonances with spin exceeding one (Fig. 13-1).

Some idea of the effect of the Froissart bound can be gained from the rate at which a non-relativistic α could increase below threshold (10-18):

$$\frac{d\,(\alpha(t) + \frac{1}{2})^2}{dq_t^2} = R^2 \tag{13-15}$$

(in the units used in (10-18), $2m = 1$ so $E = q^2$. R is a measure of the spatial extent of the bound state; for its precise definition, see (10-18)). In strong interactions, R is of the order of a pion Compton wavelength. Threshold in the t-channel also occurs at a few pion masses, so extrapolating (13-15) somewhat, we guess that the Froissart limit at $t \leq 0$ can have an appreciable effect on what we see in the t-channel. In nuclear or atomic scattering, R is relatively large and threshold in the t-channel corresponds to a large mass, so the Froissart limit has little effect.

This is also a good place to complete the earlier discussion (Chapter 4) of the convergence of the Born expansion in potential scattering. We had established that n iterations give A_{st} and A_t exactly for $t < (n+1)^2 t_o$, t_o being the "threshold" of the potential cut. In other words, the Born series for A_{st} and A_t certainly converges for all coupling strengths. When $\text{Re}\,\alpha$ exceeds zero, however, the Born series for $A_t \sim t^{\alpha} = \exp(\alpha\, \ell n\, t) = 1 + \alpha\, \ell n\, t + \ldots.$ no longer converges uniformly at large t, so the Born series for the integral over A_t (i.e., the full amplitude) breaks down.

Going back to the quantities A_t and A_{st}, for which the Born series converges, we can express these as discontinuities of the Sommerfeld-Watson representation (13-12). To calculate α and β for the leading Regge pole, then, one can simply calculate the Born series for A_t at large t, where the leading pole dominates.[68]

XIV. SOME EXPERIMENTAL RESULTS AT HIGH ENERGIES

To set the stage for the application of Regge poles at high energies, it is helpful to review certain experimental facts[84] and some concepts introduced by Pomeranchuk.

Total elastic cross sections such as $\sigma_{tot}(pp)$, $\sigma_{tot}(p\bar{p})$, $\sigma_{tot}(\pi p)$, and $\sigma_{tot}(Kp)$ are very roughly constant above a few BeV. In fact, cosmic-ray data shows no great change in $\sigma_{tot}(pp)$ and $\sigma_{tot}(\pi p)$ up to 10^4 BeV. The dependence on isotopic spin is rather weak and charge-exchange cross sections are quite small at high energies. Also, cross sections involving antiparticles, such as $\sigma_{tot}(p\bar{p})$, give some signs of approaching the particle cross sections (i.e., $\sigma_{tot}(pp)$).

According to the optical theorem

$$\mathrm{Im}\, A^T(s+i\epsilon,\, 0) = A_s{}^T(s,0) = \frac{q_s\, s^{1/2}}{8\pi}\, \sigma_{tot}{}^T(s) \tag{14-1}$$

where T is a given isotopic spin (if ordinary spin is present, A^T is the non-spin flip forward amplitude). Therefore, the imaginary part of the forward elastic amplitude is roughly proportional to s at high energy.

At small angles, the differential elastic cross sections fall off rapidly, as in diffraction scattering from a disc with radius of the order $\hbar/m_\pi c$ (later an important qualification to this picture will be described). This impression can be checked by seeing if the amplitude is essentially imaginary. The amplitude for a partial wave

$$f_\ell = \frac{n_\ell\, e^{2i\delta_\ell} - 1}{2i} \tag{14-2}$$

would be purely imaginary if the outgoing wave were totally absorbed ($n_\ell = 0$). Actually, strongly interacting particles cannot be represented by a totally absorbing disc with sharp edges (that would disagree with experiment and also violate the continuity implied by dispersion relations), but still it is the imaginary part of the amplitude which is directly built up by absorptive processes (14-1).

To perform the check one needs to measure the total cross section, which allows a calculation of $\text{Im } A^T(s,0)$ by (14-1), and the elastic cross section at zero degrees, which should check with the cross section estimated from $|\text{Im } A^T|^2$ alone. This method, while not very precise, confirms that the forward elastic amplitude is mostly imaginary at high energies.

Pomeranchuk has advanced physical arguments which connect some of these results and suggest that the trends observed at present energies should turn into exact relationships in the high-energy limit.

Pomeranchuk Rule I:[85] Assume that total cross sections for strong interactions approach constants (approximately at least). All inelastic processes compete for the constant σ_{tot}, therefore Pomeranchuk guesses that each inelastic cross section vanishes in the high-energy limit. Two-body charge-exchange reactions, such as $\pi^- + p \rightarrow \pi^0 + n$, are also inelastic, so their cross sections go to zero. In terms of isotopic spin, this implies that the high-energy limit for two-body cross sections is independent of isotopic spin, e.g.,

$$\lim_{s \to \infty} \sigma^{T=0}(\pi + \pi \to \pi + \pi) = \sigma^{T=1}(\pi + \pi \to \pi + \pi) = \sigma^{T=2}(\pi + \pi \to \pi + \pi) \quad , \tag{14-3}$$

$$\lim_{s \to \infty} \sigma^{T=1/2}(\pi + N \to \pi + N) = \sigma^{T=3/2}(\pi + N \to \pi + N) \quad . \tag{14-4}$$

Pomeranchuk Rule II:[86] As already pointed out, the real part of the forward elastic amplitude should not grow arbitrarily larger than the imaginary part. The second Pomeranchuk rule is derived by combining this condition with the forward scattering dispersion relation. The details are as follows. According to the one-dimensional dispersion relation (5-27), the real part of the forward elastic amplitude for spinless particles is

$$\operatorname{Re} A(s,o,u) = \text{const.} + \frac{(s-s_o)}{\pi} \text{ P.V.} \int \frac{ds' \, A_s(s', t=0)}{(s'-s)\,(s'-s_o)}$$

$$+ \frac{(u-u_o)}{\pi} \text{ P.V.} \int \frac{du' \, A_u(u', t=0)}{(u'-u)\,(u'-u_o)} \quad . \tag{14-5}$$

In view of the optical theorem (14-1), this becomes

$$\operatorname{Re} A(s,o,u) = \text{const.} + \frac{(s-s_o)}{8\pi^2} \text{ P.V.} \int^{\infty} \frac{ds' \, q_{s'} \, s'^{1/2} \, \sigma_{1\,tot}(s')}{(s'-s)\,(s'-s_o)}$$

$$+ \frac{(u-u_o)}{8\pi^2} \text{ P.V.} \int^{\infty} \frac{du' \, q_{u'} \, u'^{1/2} \, \sigma_{3\,tot}(u')}{(u'-u)\,(u'-u_o)} \tag{14-6}$$

where σ_1 and σ_3 are cross sections in channels I and III respectively. At zero momentum transfer, there is only one independent variable; s and u are related to the masses of the two elastically scattered particles by

$$s + u = 2M^2 + 2m^2 \quad . \tag{14-7}$$

Thus, everything can be expressed in terms of the one variable

$$\nu = \frac{(s-u)}{4M} \tag{14-8}$$

which has the significance of "laboratory energy" (total energy of the particle of mass m when the particle of mass M is at rest) in channel I and the negative of laboratory energy for channel III. With the help of the relation

$$q_s\, s^{1/2} = (\nu^2 - m^2)^{1/2}\, M \quad , \tag{14-9}$$

and with $s_o = u_o$, one finds

$$\mathrm{Re}\, A(\nu) = A(0) + \frac{M\nu}{8\pi^2}\ \mathrm{P.V.} \int_m^\infty \frac{d\nu'\,(\nu'^2 - m^2)^{1/2}}{\nu'} \left[\frac{\sigma_{1\ tot}(\nu')}{\nu' - \nu} - \frac{\sigma_{3\ tot}(\nu')}{\nu' + \nu}\right] \quad . \tag{14-10}$$

The integral appears to need a second subtraction because σ_{tot} is constant. Making a second subtraction, one finds

$$\lim_{\nu \to \infty} \mathrm{Re}\, A(\nu) \sim \nu\, \ell n\, \nu \lim_{\nu \to \infty} \left[\sigma_{3\ tot}(\nu) - \sigma_{1\ tot}(\nu)\right] \quad . \tag{14-11}$$

In order to keep Re A from dominating Im A, then, we must require

$$\lim_{\nu \to \infty} \left[\sigma_{3\ tot}(\nu) - \sigma_{1\ tot}(\nu)\right] = 0 \qquad (14\text{-}12)$$

which is the Pomeranchuk rule. Since the reaction in channel III is $\bar{A} + B \to \bar{A} + B$ when $A + B \to A + B$ takes place in channel I, the rule says that

$$\lim_{\nu \to \infty} \left[\sigma_{tot}(AB) - \sigma_{tot}(\bar{A}B)\right] = 0 \quad . \qquad (14\text{-}13)$$

If the rule is satisfied, then (14-10) converges with only one subtraction. A similar derivation again leads to (14-13) in the case of reactions with spin, such as πP and PP scattering.

The first Pomeranchuk rule yields the same condition as the second in πN scattering, where π^- is the antiparticle of π^+. In NN and KN scattering, the first rule relates $\sigma_{tot}(pp)$ to $\sigma_{tot}(np)$, and $\sigma_{tot}(K^+ p)$ to $\sigma_{tot}(K^0 p)$, while the second relates $\sigma_{tot}(pp)$ to $\sigma_{tot}(p\bar{p})$, $\sigma_{tot}(K^+ p)$ to $\sigma_{tot}(K^- p)$, and so forth. In $\pi\pi$ scattering, the second rule provides one non-trivial relationship $(\sigma_{tot}(\pi^+ \pi^+) = \sigma_{tot}(\pi^+ \pi^-))$, while the first rule provides that as well as one other (14-3).

Recently, experiments on elastic pp scattering at small angles[87] have added an important further piece of information on diffraction peaks at relativistic energies. In the usual picture of scattering from an object of radius R, the diffraction peak lies within an angle

$\theta \sim 1/q R$ or a momentum transfer

$$t = -2q^2 (1 - \cos\theta) \simeq -q^2 \theta^2 \simeq -R^{-2} \quad . \qquad (14\text{-}14)$$

In the pp experiments, however, the average momentum transfer appears to decrease instead of remaining constant as the energy increases (Fig. 14-1). In other words, the effective radius is increasing. At the same time, the total cross section is independent of energy, so the "transparency" of the target must also be increasing. The demonstration of how these remarkable results can be explained by exchange of a Regge pole originally gave great impetus to acceptance of the Regge pole hypothesis.*

*More recently, however, it has been found that the average momentum transfer in $\pi^{\pm}p$ scattering remains constant within the rather small experimental errors. Some discussion of the present situation is given in Addendum II.

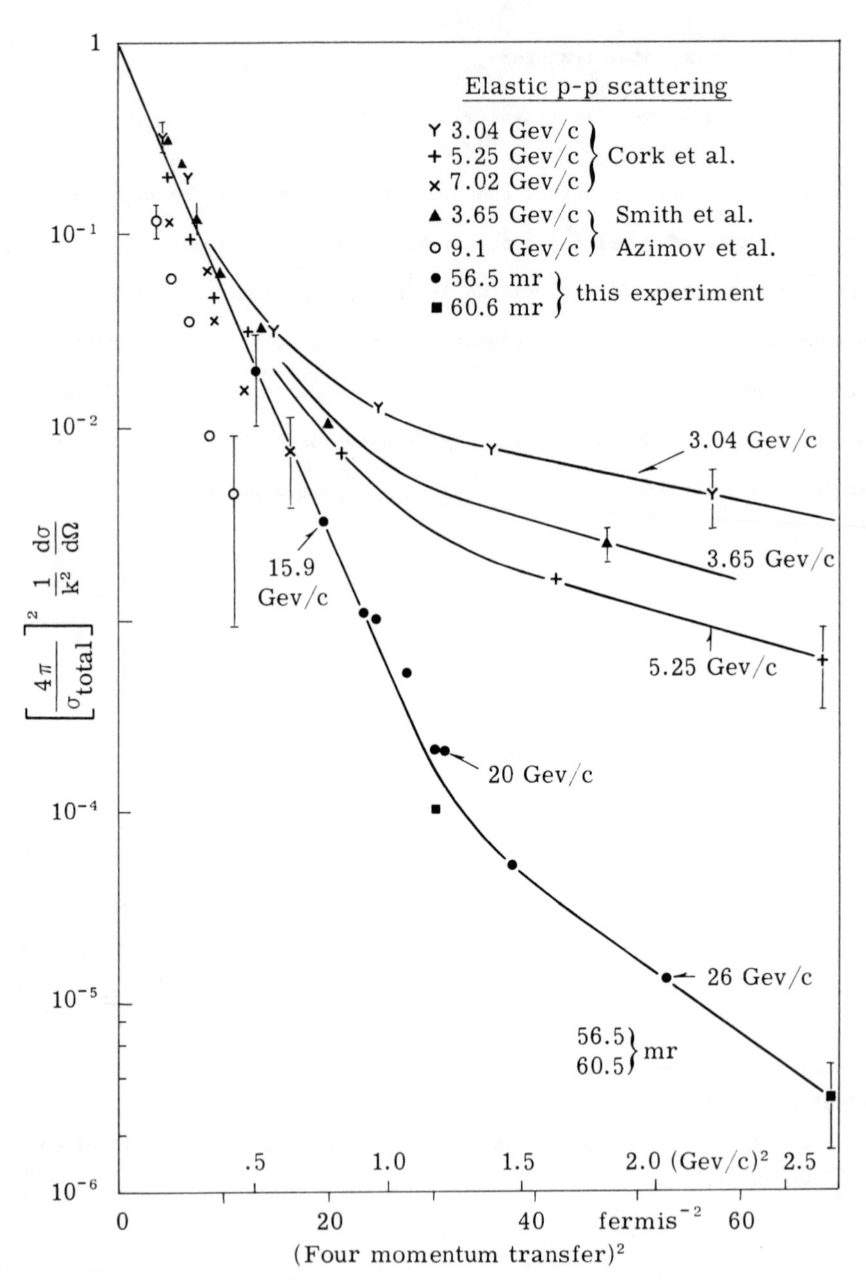

Figure 14-1 The elastic pp cross section as a function of momentum transfer, at various energies (taken from Cocconi, et al., Reference 87).

XV. REGGE POLES AND HIGH-ENERGY EXPERIMENTS

If we assume that a Sommerfeld-Watson representation holds in the t-channel, where s is momentum transfer, then the pole with maximum Re $\alpha(t)$ dominates at large s and the amplitude simplifies there to the form $A \sim s^{\alpha(t)}$. Carrying this result over to the channel where s is the energy variable, and squaring to obtain the differential cross section, one finds the form

$$\frac{d\sigma(s,t)}{dt} \sim \frac{|A|^2}{s^2} \sim f(t)\ (s)^{2\alpha(t)-2} \quad . \tag{15-1}$$

We want to describe the dominant experimental trends and Pomeranchuk rules of the previous chapter in terms of this formula, using only one Regge pole.* This dominant pole is called the Pomeranchuk pole, or Pomeranchon for short, because of its connection with diffraction scattering.

What this means in terms of diagrams can be seen in Fig. 15-1. The Pomeranchon represents an intermediate state in the t-channel, and an exchanged state from the point of view of the s-channel. Normally, we think of exchanging a particle of definite physical spin like the π or the ρ, or, in general, a sum over physical spins. But now we exchange a non-physical spin $\alpha(t)$, out of which exchanges of all physical spins could be projected if desired.

---

*Recent πp and pp experiments, and ideas about "Regge cuts", cast doubt upon the original one-pole analysis of pp scattering described in the present chapter. Since the situation is unclear and the one-pole model provides the simplest introduction to the general theory in any case, we have retained the original analysis here and discuss possible changes in Addendum II.

At what energies are the asymptotic expressions valid? A necessary requirement for each Regge pole is that $\cos\Theta_t$ be substantially greater than one, to allow the expansion $P_\alpha(-\cos\Theta_t) \sim (-\cos\Theta_t)^\alpha \sim s^\alpha$. This must be checked in each case; for example, in the equal mass case, we have

$$\cos\Theta_t = -1 - \frac{2s}{t - 4m^2} \tag{15-2}$$

which is asymptotic at small t when the lab energy becomes large compared to the rest mass. At large angles in the s-channel, the asymptotic expression cannot be used, because $t = -(s-4m^2)(1-\cos\Theta_s)/2$ grows as fast as s does and $\cos\Theta_t$ remains small. At angles near 180°, however, one can use a Sommerfeld-Watson representation in the u or "exchange" channel instead of the t or "direct" channel, and simple asymptotic expressions $A \sim s^{\alpha(u)}$ emerge. The further question of when one Regge pole begins to dominate the rest cannot be decided on purely kinematic grounds and has to be handled phenomenologically at present.

Equation (15-1) provides a simple prediction for the ratio of cross sections at the same momentum transfer but different energies:

$$\frac{\frac{d\sigma}{dt}(s_1,t)}{\frac{d\sigma}{dt}(s_2,t)} = \left(\frac{s_1}{s_2}\right)^{2\alpha(t)-1} . \tag{15-3}$$

The first reaction on which it was possible to test (15-3) was $p + p \rightarrow p + p$.[87] At $t = 0$, the constancy of the total cross section and the optical theorem $(\mathrm{Im}\, A \sim s\,\sigma_{tot})$ ensure that $\alpha(0) = 1$. The data between $t = 0$ and $t = -1\ \mathrm{BeV}^2$ are consistent with an α decreasing to 0:

$$\alpha(t) = 1 + \frac{t}{50m_\pi^2} \quad , \qquad -1 \text{ BeV}^2 \leq t \leq 0 \quad . \tag{15-4}$$

At larger momentum transfers, the errors on α are large and the situation is not clear.

The slope $d\alpha/dt$ obtained in the region $-1(\text{BeV})^2 \leq t \leq 0$ is of order $1/50m_\pi^2$. If we take the optimistic step of comparing this with the non-relativistic expression (13-15) for $d\alpha/dq_t^2$, and use the connection $dt = 4dq_t^2$, we obtain a radius for the "bound Regge state" of order $R \sim \hbar/2m_\pi c$, a very reasonable result.

Another way to view the situation is to study (15-1) at fixed s as t varies. Combining (15-1) and (15-4), we have:

$$\frac{d\sigma}{dt} \quad f(t) \exp\left[-2\,\alpha'(0)\,|t|\,\ell n\, s\right] \qquad (-1 \text{ BeV}^2 \leq t \leq 0) \quad . \tag{15-5}$$

At fixed s, Eq. (15-5) falls off exponentially with increasing momentum transfer, as in a normal diffraction peak. The new feature is the logarithmic narrowing of the diffraction peak as s increases.

There is some evidence that the same qualitative features appear in the reaction $p + p \rightarrow p + N^*$, where N^* is one of the $I = 1/2$ πN resonances.[87)] More detailed experiments are needed, however, to show whether (15-1) is satisfied with precision in this reaction and elastic pp scattering.

Thus far, we have determined the t-dependence of the Pomeranchuk trajectory from the angular dependence of the diffraction peak. The quantum numbers of this trajectory can also be determined, from the behavior of total cross sections as summarized by the Pomeranchuk rules (which we assume to be correct).

Pomeranchuk Rule I: We have seen the result of exchanging the Pomeranchon between two protons. If we assign the Pomeranchon isotopic spin zero, strangeness zero, and baryon number zero, then it cannot lead to charge exchange scattering. It can, however, be exchanged in $\pi + N \to \pi + N$, $\pi + \pi \to \pi + \pi$, $K + N \to K + N$, as long as no charge exchange occurs. Thus, if the Pomeranchuk trajectory dominates at small t, all elastic cross sections are constant in the high-energy limit (due to exchange of Pomeranchon with $\alpha_p(0) = 1$) and all charge-exchange cross sections go to zero (the highest power $\alpha(t)$ associated with charge-exchange is < 1). The prediction is made that all diffraction peaks are characterized by the same α_p.

Pomeranchuk Rule II: The Pomeranchon can be thought of as an intermediate state in, say, the t-channel. As we discussed in Chapter 13, it has to be assigned a definite parity, even or odd. To satisfy Pomeranchuk's second rule, the Pomeranchon must be taken as an even state:

$$\frac{\beta(t)}{\sin \pi\alpha_p(t)} \left[P_{\alpha_p(t)}(-\cos \Theta_t) + P_{\alpha_p(t)}(\cos \Theta_t) \right] \quad . \qquad (15\text{-}6)$$

The details of (15-6) are as follows. The first Legendre polynomial has the discontinuity $-2i \sin \pi \alpha P_\alpha(\cos \Theta_t)$ at $\cos \Theta_t \geq 1$ (i.e., at positive s for $t \leq 0$); the second Legendre polynomial has the discontinuity $+ 2i \sin \pi \alpha P_\alpha(-\cos \theta_t)$ at $\cos \theta_t \leq -1$ (i.e., at positive u for $t \leq 0$). The factor $\sin \pi\alpha$ is not surprising because the discontinuity of s^α must vanish at integer α. The imaginary part of (15-6) at large positive s ($t \leq 0$) is then $-i \beta(t) P_{\alpha_p(t)}(\cos \theta_t)$, which behaves linearly in s as $\alpha_p \to 1$ at $t = 0$. In the real part of (15-6), there is a cancellation between $-\cos \theta_t$ and $\cos \theta_t$ which leaves a term that is negligible at large s. Thus the choice of even states makes the amplitude purely imaginary at high energy, as is appropriate for diffraction scattering (note that this is true only at $t = 0$). The imaginary part of (15-6) in the u-channel is $i \beta P_{\alpha_p}(-\cos \theta_t)$. At $t = 0$, this becomes the same as in the s-channel so the optical theorem makes the total cross sections the same:

$$\sigma_{tot}(A + B \to A + B) = \sigma_{tot}(A + \bar{B} \to A + \bar{B}) \quad . \tag{15-7}$$

In the previous discussion of Pomeranchuk Rule II similar features, Eq. (15-7) and a cancellation between real parts emerged from a different viewpoint.

It has already been noted that high-energy elastic amplitudes grow with the highest power permitted by the Froissart limit in the physical region. This has been cast into a principle: "The strong interactions are as strong as possible." [4] In terms of Regge trajectories, this implies that the highest trajectory at $t = 0$ -- $\alpha_p(0)$ --

lies at the Froissart limit. At negative t, α_p must fall below the limit because of the general property $\frac{d\alpha}{dt} > 0$. Some clue as to why the strength is maximal may be guessed from the properties of the diffraction peak. In general, $A \sim s^{\alpha}$ is complex at large s; the only exceptions are $\alpha_p = 1, 3, 5, \ldots$. The only one of these permitted by the Froissart limit is $\alpha_p = 1$. Thus, maximal strength may have something to do with maintaining diffraction in a consistent way.

At $t \simeq -1\ (\text{BeV})^2$, α_p seems to pass through zero (15-4). Normally, the pole of $\left[\sin \pi\alpha\right]^{-1}$ would be interpreted as a particle in the t-channel, but in this case $t = m^2$ is negative. Furthermore, the pole appears in a physical region for the s-channel, where there should be no singularities, and where, in fact, the cross section does vary smoothly. One likely explanation is that β vanishes at the pole to maintain consistency. Gell-Mann[63)] has found an analogy with nuclear physics where the ground state may be $J = 7/2$, for example. He shows that in such a case $J = 3/2$ is likely to be pure $\ell = -1$, for example, and β would vanish at $J = 3/2$ to avoid a physical state with this "nonsensical value" of ℓ. Correspondingly, the Pomeranchuk trajectory may be pure $\ell = -1$ at $J = 0$, and thus require $\beta = 0$. What is needed to test this idea is a detailed dynamical theory of the coupling of the Pomeranchon to states with spin, such as $\rho + \rho$, $\omega + \omega$, $N + \bar{N}$, ... (presumably the low mass states are especially important).

In general, one would expect further Regge poles besides the one responsible for diffraction. The Pomeranchuk trajectory was associated with isotopic spin 0, baryon number 0, and strangeness 0. Other trajectories should have a variety of other quantum numbers. Consider the u-channel amplitude for $\pi + N \to \pi + N$ as an example. It is a sum over isotopic spins $I = 1/2$ and $3/2$, spins $J = \ell \pm 1/2$, and even and odd parity. Since the strong interaction for this channel depends on all these quantum numbers and does not mix them, each of the eight possible states of I, $J - \ell$, and parity should have its own independent set of Regge poles, which are summed over to obtain the complete amplitude. To illustrate this complicated state of affairs, we list the usual assignments for the first few πN isobars, together with the quantum numbers expected for the next member of each family:

$$
\begin{array}{llll}
940 \text{ MeV} & N_1 : & T = 1/2, \; P_{1/2} \to T = 1/2, \; F_{5/2} \\
1220 \text{ MeV} & N_3^* : & T = 3/2, \; P_{3/2} \to T = 3/2, \; F_{7/2} \\
1510 \text{ MeV} & N_1^* : & T = 1/2, \; D_{3/2} \to T = 1/2, \; G_{7/2} \\
1690 \text{ MeV} & N_1^{**} : & T = 1/2, \; F_{5/2} \quad \text{(nucleon family?)}
\end{array}
$$

Not until the third resonance do we have any evidence for the second member of a family.

Thus the amplitude in each channel is a sum over amplitudes with different quantum numbers, each of which can be transformed from a partial-wave expansion into a Sommerfeld-Watson representation. In addition, crossing allows us to start with the partial-wave expansion in any channel -- s, t, or u. Which expansion is most useful depends on the problem. For example, consider scattering in the s-channel. At small s, one normally uses the s-channel partial-wave expansion. At large s, this fails to converge well, but at forward angles (small t), $\cos\Theta_t$ becomes large and it is convenient to employ the Sommerfeld-Watson representation for the t-channel amplitude. For backward angles (small u), $\cos\Theta_u$ becomes large and the Sommerfeld-Watson representation for the u-channel is best.*

One way to study trajectories other than the Pomeranchuk is to find processes where the Pomeranchon cannot be exchanged.

Example: Backward $\pi + p$ scattering. All the πN isobar families can be exchanged. If one of these trajectories dominates, $d\sigma/du$ obeys an expression similar to (15-5), and one should see a rapidly decreasing backward peak. The cross section at fixed u probably falls off rapidly with energy ($d\sigma/du \sim s^{2\alpha(u)-2}$) because $\alpha(u)$ decreases from $u \geq m_p^2$ to $u < 0$, in vivid contrast to exchange of, say, the $J = 3/2$ resonance by itself, which would give $d\sigma/du \sim s^{2J-2} \sim s$.

---

*If some external masses are unequal, as in πN scattering, there is a small cone of momentum transfers (around $u = 0$ in the πN example) where neither $\cos\Theta_t$ or $\cos\Theta_u$ is large, and the asymptotic Regge expressions fail to apply. The cone vanishes as $s/m^2 \to \infty$.

<u>Example</u>: Backward n + p scattering (charge exchange). Only T = 1 exchange is possible, so the experimental cross section is sensitive to exchange of Regge states with that quantum number. Again, a backward peak is expected.

<u>Example</u>: The reaction $p + p \to p + N^*$, where N^* is a πN resonance, can proceed by exchange of the Pomeranchon if N^* has $I = 1/2$, but the 3-3 resonance requires an exchange of $I = 1$ (a π or ρ, for example). Since α_π and α_ρ are less than α_p, production of the 3-3 resonance should fall off relatively rapidly with increasing energy, and the data bears this out.[87)]

Trajectories with baryon number and strangeness zero may also be seen in interference with the Pomeranchuk term. If several Regge terms with $\alpha_1(t)$, $\alpha_2(t)$, . . . are exchanged, the amplitude in the s-channel has the form:

$$A(s,t) \sim b_1(t)\, s^{\alpha_1(t)} + b_2(t)\, s^{\alpha_2(t)} + \ldots \qquad (15\text{-}8)$$

At very high s, one sees only the term with the highest α, but at sufficiently low s the other terms interfere appreciably. It is especially simple to apply (15-8) at $t = 0$ for elastic reactions, where the imaginary part of the amplitude is directly proportional to the total cross section on account of the optical theorem (14-1). One finds:

$$\sigma_{tot}(s) \sim \mathrm{Im}\, b_1(0)\, s^{\alpha_1(0)-1} + \mathrm{Im}\, b_2(0)\, s^{\alpha_2(0)-1} + \dots \quad (15\text{-}9)$$

The first term is the Pomeranchuk term, which is the same for particle and antiparticle reactions: $pp \to pp$ and $\bar{p}p \to \bar{p}p$, for example. The second term might be the ω-meson trajectory, for example; in this case it turns out that:[75]

$$\sigma_{tot}^{pp}(s) \sim \mathrm{Im}\, b_P(0)\, s^{\alpha_P(0)-1} + \mathrm{Im}\, b_\omega(0)\, s^{\alpha_\omega(0)-1} + \dots , \quad (15\text{-}10)$$

$$\sigma_{tot}^{\bar{p}p}(s) \sim \mathrm{Im}\, b_P(0)\, s^{\alpha_P(0)-1} - \mathrm{Im}\, b_\omega(0)\, s^{\alpha_\omega(0)-1} + \dots \quad (15\text{-}11)$$

The observed difference between pp and $\bar{p}p$ cross sections at high energy can then be attributed to persistent contributions from exchange of the ω trajectory -- and other trajectories which have quantum numbers that distinguish between protons and antiprotons (the Pomeranchuk trajectory, with $T = 0$, even parity, etc., cannot make the distinction). Udgaonkar[75] has analyzed the data on $\sigma^{pp} - \sigma^{\bar{p}p}$, $\sigma^{\pi^+ p} - \sigma^{\pi^- p}$, and $\sigma^{K^+ p} - \sigma^{K^- p}$ in this fashion and obtains estimates for some of the Regge trajectories. Igi[88] has used (15-9) in conjunction with the dispersion relations for forward πN scattering, and finds that in addition to the Pomeranchon he needs another contribution with the same quantum numbers and $\alpha(0) > 0$.

Further predictions follow from the observation that the Regge residues $\beta(t)$ factorize. This property is similar to the behavior of a one-particle exchange -- for example, exchange of a π between n and p, which factors into a πnn coupling and a πpp coupling. In the same way, the residue $\beta(t)$ for Fig. 15-1 factors into an $AA\alpha$ vertex function and a $BB\alpha$ vertex function.

The factorization was proved by Gell-Mann,[89] using the Schrödinger equation, and by Gribov and Pomeranchuk,[76] using unitarity directly. We shall give Gell-Mann's proof. Consider a number N of coupled Schrödinger equations with common angular momentum:

$$\left(\frac{d^2}{dr^2} + q_i^2 - \frac{\ell(\ell+1)}{r^2}\right) \psi_i(r) = \sum_{j=1}^{N} V_{ij}(r)\, \psi_j(r) \quad . \tag{15-12}$$

The S-matrix S_{ij} is defined by taking solutions "regular" at the origin in all channels $(\psi_i \propto r_i^{\ell+1})$ and asymptotic to:

$$e^{-iq_i r} - e^{iq_i r}\, e^{-i\ell\pi}\, S_{ii} \qquad \text{in channel } i \quad , \tag{15-13}$$

$$- e^{iq_j r}\, e^{-i\ell\pi}\, S_{ij} \left(\frac{q_i}{q_j}\right)^{1/2} \qquad \text{in channels } j \neq i \quad . \tag{15-14}$$

A Regge pole corresponds to a value of ℓ (in general, complex) for which some or all of the S_{ij} are infinite. The infinity arises because there exists a wave function (for that ℓ) asymptotic to:

$$e^{iq_j r} \quad f_j \quad q_j^{-1/2} \qquad \text{in all channels} \quad . \tag{15-15}$$

Except accidentally, not more than one such function will exist for that ℓ and fixed energy. Near the pole, then, we have:

$$f_i/f_j = S_{1i}/S_{1j} = S_{2i}/S_{2j} \cdot \cdot \cdot \cdot \tag{15-16}$$

As a consequence of (15-16), S_{ij} factors into a number depending on i times one depending on j.

In the channel where the pole represents an intermediate state (t-channel in Fig. 15-1), this result is closely related to the factorization into partial widths in the compound nucleus model of nuclear reactions. In the channel where the pole is exchanged (s-channel in Fig. 15-1), the factorization leads to new predictions about high-energy behavior. For elastic scattering of particles A and B, exchange of the Pomeranchon gives a constant cross section in the limit $s \to \infty$:

$$\sigma_{tot}(A,B) \to \text{Im } b_{AA\ P\ BB}(t = 0) \quad . \tag{15-17}$$

But since b(0) factors, so does the asymptotic value of σ_{tot}. We then have:

$$\sigma_{tot}(A,B) \to g_{AAP} \quad g_{BBP} \quad . \tag{15-18}$$

Therefore, the three cross sections for A + A, A + B, and B + B depend on only two coupling parameters. If A is the pion and B the nucleon, for example, we can deduce:

$$\sigma_{\pi\pi} = \frac{|\sigma_{\pi N}|^2}{\sigma_{NN}} \quad . \tag{15-19}$$

Of course, it is difficult to check this relation because the pion is unstable!

An interesting alternative to Regge poles is the possibility that fixed spins $J = 0, 1/2$, or 1 are exchanged. In earlier chapters, this possibility was connected with exchange of "elementary particles" that do not lie on Regge trajectories. At present, pp scattering gives no indication of terms with fixed $J = 1$. If such terms exist, associated for example with exchange of an "elementary" ω, their coupling to protons is severely limited.

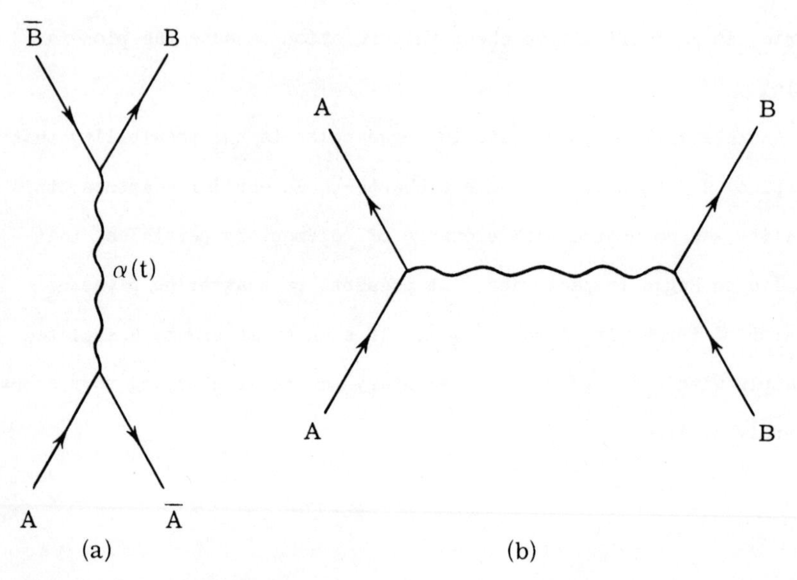

Figure 15-1 Diagrams representing an intermediate Regge state with spin $\alpha(t)$ in the t-channel, from the point of view of: (a) scattering in the t-channel; (b) scattering in the s-channel.

XVI. ARE ALL STRONGLY INTERACTING PARTICLES COMPOSITE?

In the usual picture of atomic or nuclear physics, a very large number of composite atoms and nuclei are made up of electrons, neutrons, and protons. The electron, neutron, and proton are treated as elementary because most phenomena involve energies too low to excite their internal structure. In high-energy physics, on the other hand, the range of energies easily allows excitation and breakup of any particle. This circumstance motivated Chew and Frautschi[72)] to conjecture that they should all be treated on the same basis. At the same time, the forces in high-energy physics are caused by exchange of the very particles one is trying to explain, whereas atomic and nuclear forces are viewed as arising from exchange of elementary photons and mesons. To summarize, atoms and nuclei are usually thought of as compounds of elementary particles held together by exchange of other elementary particles, whereas we conjecture that baryons and mesons are compounds of baryons and mesons held together in a self-consistent way by exchange of baryons and mesons.

Composite particles can be described usefully by Regge poles. Therefore, in its technical form, the Chew-Frautschi conjecture says that <u>all</u> strongly interacting particles lie on Regge trajectories. In the complex angular momentum plane, this means there are no terms at fixed $J = 0, 1/2$, or 1; only moving Regge poles. Back in the complex s, t, u-plane, it implies no independent subtraction terms of the CDD type discussed in Chapters 3 and 5; all singularities follow from unitarity. In other words, we are conjecturing "maximal analyticity" in energy, momentum transfer, and angular momentum.

If all strongly interacting particles lie on Regge trajectories, there is hope that their coupling constants and mass ratios can be determined from unitarity and maximal analyticity requirements. The way towards fulfilling this hope is believed to lie in the further development of the self-consistent or "bootstrap" method of calculation which was described in Chapter 7.

Bootstrap calculations lean heavily on "crossing", a concept obtained by combining quantum mechanics and special relativity. Thus, determination of the strong interaction couplings and masses would represent a further understanding of how small and restrictive is the overlap between these two theories. Historically, the study of this overlap already led to the necessary connections between particles and antiparticles, between spin and statistics, and the TCP theorem. There is, in fact, no reason why the chain of restrictions must stop at the strong interaction masses and couplings; the conservation laws and weaker interactions might also be implicated. On the other hand, it is hard to believe that a complete picture can emerge until at least the further conditions implied by general relativity are brought into play!

To return to slightly more solid ground: according to our conjecture, we can draw Regge trajectories passing through all strongly interacting particles (all taken in the t-channel for convenience) as in Fig. 16-1.[5] For orientation purposes, we give each term a slope of the same order of magnitude, since $d(\alpha + \frac{1}{2})^2/dq_t^2 \sim R^2$ and the spatial extent of all states is expected to be of order $R \sim \hbar/2m_\pi c$. Of course, this is only a rough approximation; eventually, we expect the trajectories will turn over, and we know that the slope of $\mathrm{Re}\,\ell$ changes abruptly at a two-particle threshold when ℓ is small (Eq. 10-40).

The conjecture embodied in Fig. 16-1 has many interesting consequences. Although the Pomeranchuk trajectory was first discovered via its high-energy effects in the crossed channels, if it continues to rise it may lead to a spin 2 meson (T = 0, B = 0, S = 0, G = +) with a mass of order 1 BeV. It appears that a resonance with these quantum numbers does occur at 1250 MeV.[90,91] In a couple of other cases, it is also possible to estimate the slope of a trajectory. For ω, one can estimate α (t = 0) from the rate of approach of total cross sections to the Pomeranchuk limit.[75] The nucleon (T = 1/2, $P_{1/2}$, 939 MeV) may lie on the same trajectory as the third πN resonance (T = 1/2, $F_{5/2}$, 1688 MeV) (remember that exchange potentials lead to a split into "even" and "odd" trajectories (Eq. 13-7), each of which has physical states only at intervals $\Delta J = 2$). It is also possible[92] that the 3-3 resonance (T = 3/2, $P_{3/2}$, 1238 MeV) lies on the same trajectory as the 1922-MeV πN resonance (T = 3/2, $F_{7/2}$?), and that the Λ^o (T = 0, $P_{1/2}$, 1115 MeV) may be grouped with the Y_o^* (T = 0, $F_{5/2}$?, 1815 MeV). In all these cases, the slope seems to be of the same order as the slope of the Pomeranchuk trajectory. It is hoped that studies of the higher-mass baryon and meson resonances will reveal more trajectories that lead to at least two physical states.

CDD poles could also be represented in Fig. 16-1, where they would appear as horizontal lines with J = 0, 1/2, or 1. They would not be associated with families of particles with increasing J, and when exchanged they would tend to produce forward (or backward) peaks of fixed width in t. As we have already mentioned, however, the maximal analyticity conjecture cannot tolerate CDD poles and insists that we treat all spins on the same footing.

A very striking empirical feature of Fig. 16-1 is that trajectories with high quantum numbers tend to lie below those with low quantum numbers. For example, a number of mesons ($B = 0$) lie above the first baryon trajectory ($B = 1$), and the trajectories associated with nuclei ($B > 1$) are way out of sight to the right. Within each class, $B = 0$ or $B = 1$, the first trajectory with non-zero strangeness (K or Λ) lies below some trajectories with zero strangeness. No extremely high quantum numbers appear at all. The highest trajectory -- the Pomeranchuk trajectory -- has $T = 0$, $B = 0$, $S = 0$, even parity -- in short, the quantum numbers of the vacuum.

In $\pi\pi$ scattering, it is possible to find a dynamical explanation of why the trajectory with $T = 0$ lies higher than trajectories with $T = 1$ (i.e., the ρ meson) or $T = 2$. We have previously defined the "generalized potential" for the s-channel in terms of discontinuities in the other two channels (Chapter 6). In particular, the long-range potential arose from exchange of two-pion states. The weight function of the potential for an isotopic spin T state in the s-channel was given in terms of exchange of two-pion T' states by:

$$V_{2\pi}^{T}(t,s) = \sum_{T'=0,1,2} \beta_{TT'} A_t^{(el)T'}(t,s) \tag{7-11}$$

where the crossing matrix β had the form:

$$\beta_{TT'} = \begin{pmatrix} 1/3 & 1 & 5/3 \\ 1/3 & 1/2 & -5/6 \\ 1/3 & -1/2 & 1/6 \end{pmatrix} \quad . \tag{7-12}$$

Exchanges of four pions and heavier configurations add to the potential and are described by the same crossing matrix.

From the elements of the crossing matrix (7-12), it turns out that all contributions to $V^{T=0}$ are attractive and stronger than (or at least as strong as) in the other two isotopic spin states. The strongest element in the long-range potential is exchange of the ρ ($T' = 1$, $J = 1$ resonance), which provides a weaker but still attractive potential for the $T = 1$ state and a repulsive potential for the $T = 2$ state. All this is in agreement with Fig. 16-1, where $\alpha_{T=0}(t) > \alpha_{T=1}(t)$ and $\alpha_{T=2}(t)$ fails to appear at all.

In more complicated cases, it is not as yet possible to understand the ordering of trajectories in detail. However, it is possible to give a physical argument for the ordering of $\alpha_i(t)$ at $t = 0$ in terms of the high-energy peaks in the s-channel. These peaks evidently are a result of coherence in scattering. Maximum coherence -- i.e., the maximum value of $\alpha_i(0)$ -- occurs for exchange of the quantum numbers of the vacuum, which leave the outgoing state coherent with the incoming state. The degree of coherence progressively decreases with an increase in the quantum numbers of the exchanged system -- with a subsequent decrease in the value of $\alpha_i(0)$. By analytic continuation, such a correlation between $\alpha_i(0)$ and internal quantum numbers is likely to be maintained for $\alpha_i(t)$ in the region of positive t, with the consequence that low-energy bound states and resonances are most likely to occur for low isotopic spin, strangeness, and baryon number. Whereas exchange of non-zero strangeness or baryon number is certain to lead to incoherence, exchange of non-zero isotopic spin has some probability of leading to a coherent final state by the vector addition rule, so the ordering of quantum numbers is expected to be relatively weak for isotopic spin.

It may be noted that a theory with no arbitrary dimensionless parameters _must_ be a theory of _strong interactions_. If the interactions were weak, the "potentials" would be weak and the elastic discontinuities calculated from the potentials would be doubly weak. But these elastic discontinuities provide a potential for a crossed channel, and if we proceed in this manner the potentials get steadily weaker after each round of iterations and the solution tends to zero. The potentials must be strong to maintain a self-consistent calculation. When arbitrary subtraction terms were present, there was no difficulty of this kind, for the arbitrary subtraction terms did not have to be determined in a self-consistent way.

In conclusion, we list some unsolved problems:

i) Better methods of treating inelastic scattering are needed. Our lack of understanding of inelastic scattering limits bootstrap and other dynamical calculations. On the level of principle, it has thwarted proofs of the Mandelstam representation and Regge pole hypothesis, as well as attempts to remove the relativistic divergence problem.

ii) Thus far, S-matrix theory has improved our understanding of dynamics, but not of conservation laws and symmetry principles. Will any of the conservation laws emerge from the requirement of a self-consistent S-matrix?

iii) Do electrons, muons, photons, and neutrinos lie on Regge trajectories?[90] If they are bound states, where is there an attraction strong enough to bind them?

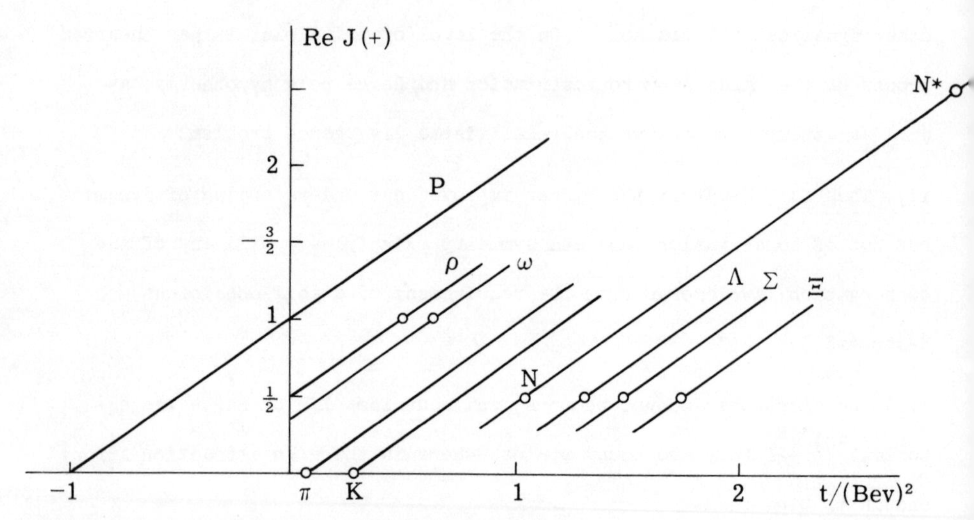

Figure 16-1 Schematic drawing of Regge trajectories for some of the strongly interacting particles.

ADDENDUM I
THE KHURI-JONES THRESHOLD FACTOR

In the Sommerfeld-Watson representation (10-24), the amplitude A depends on momentum transfer through the factor

$$P_\alpha(-\cos\theta) = P_\alpha(-1 - \frac{t}{2q^2}) \tag{A-1}$$

which has a branch point at $t = 0$. This contrasts with the Mandelstam representation where the first branch point of A, at $t = m^2$, depends on the lightest exchanged mass m, and the cut of A_s has a curved boundary. Thus, the sum over Regge poles and the background integral must cancel the cuts that extend to $t = 0$ in individual terms.

Partial wave amplitudes

$$A_\ell = \frac{e^{i\delta} \sin\delta}{q} \tag{A-2}$$

should behave like $\mathrm{Re}\, A_\ell \sim q^{2\ell}$ and $\mathrm{Im}\, A_\ell \sim q^{4\ell+1}$ near threshold. As pointed out in Chapter 4, correct threshold behavior for $\mathrm{Re}\, A_\ell$ follows automatically from the Mandelstam representation with A cut at $t = m^2$, and correct behavior for $\mathrm{Im}\, A_\ell$ follows from the curved boundary of A_{st}. Since individual Regge terms do not have properly located cuts, it is no surprise that the projection of a Regge pole onto a partial wave gives incorrect threshold behavior. The partial wave projection is

$$A_\ell(q) = \frac{\beta(q)}{\pi\left[\alpha(q) - \ell\right]\left[\alpha(q) + \ell + 1\right]} \quad . \tag{10-36}$$

The residue β varies like[56,61]

$$\beta \sim q^{2\alpha} \tag{A-3}$$

with the badly behaved result

$$A_\ell(q) \sim \frac{q^{2\alpha(0)}}{\pi\left[\alpha(0) - \ell\right]\left[\alpha(0) + \ell + 1\right]} \quad . \tag{A-4}$$

A useful advance was made by Khuri[97] and Jones,[98] who wrote a modified Sommerfeld-Watson representation. In the new representation, each Regge pole term is a former pole term with some background integral added in such a way as to cancel the cut between $t = 0$ and $t = m^2$, although the correct curved boundary of A_{st} is still not achieved. One virtue of the new representation is the very simple form taken by the projection of a "new Regge pole term" onto a partial wave: β in (10-36) is simply replaced by $\beta \exp\left[-(\ell-\alpha)\,\xi\right]$, where

$$\xi = \ln\left[1 + \frac{m^2}{2q^2} + \left\{\left(1 + \frac{m^2}{2q^2}\right)^2 - 1\right\}^{1/2}\right] \quad . \tag{A-5}$$

As q^2 approaches zero, we find

$$\beta\, e^{-(\ell-\alpha)\xi} \sim q^{2\alpha}\, e^{-(\ell-\alpha)\ln m^2/q^2} \sim q^{2\ell} \tag{A-6}$$

so the threshold behavior of $\mathrm{Re}\, A_\ell$ comes out right ($\mathrm{Im}\, A_\ell$ is still not right because the curved boundary of A_{st} is missing).

Although the complete A_ℓ has left cuts beginning at $q^2 = -m^2/4$, $-(2m)^2/4$, $-(3m)^2/4$, etc., (Chapter 4), the one-Regge pole approximation (10-36) does not. Now the square root in ξ vanishes at $q^2 = -m^2/4$, supplying $\beta \exp\left[-(\ell-\alpha)\,\xi\right]$ with a branch point at $q^2 = -m^2/4$ but not at $-(2m)^2/4$, etc.

ADDENDUM II
THE POSSIBILITY OF REGGE CUTS

After these lectures were given in June 1962, further data on pp and πp diffraction peaks were obtained and the possibility of Regge cuts was increasingly emphasized. We wish to discuss these new features and the possible relations between them, which appear to complicate the analysis of high-energy scattering presented in Chapter 15.

In the improved pp data[99] the diffraction peak shrank somewhat more slowly with increasing energy, and the width of the peak appeared to become nearly constant as energies of 30 BeV were approached, although this last point was obscured by relatively large experimental errors. The implications for the Regge pole interpretation are:

i) The slope of the Pomeranchuk trajectory was overestimated in Chapter 15. The resonance observed at 1250 MeV[90,91] can still be fit onto the trajectory without difficulty by letting $d\alpha/dt$ increase with t.

ii) The smaller slope may no longer account for all the falloff of $d\sigma/dt$ with t at fixed s in (15-5), so a rapid falloff of the residue $\beta(t)$ may be needed. One expects the rate of falloff to be related to the range of the forces, thus restoring the usual connection between range and the width of the diffraction peak (in Chapter 15, the width depended on $d\alpha/dt$, which through (13-15) depends on the range of forces in the crossed channel!).

iii) If the width of the peak really stabilizes at 30 BeV, then other terms interfere strongly with the Pomeranchon to give the more rapid shrinking at lower energies.

In the $\pi^{\pm}p$ data,[99,100] no energy variation whatever has been detected in the width of the diffraction peak, although the shrinking peak was supposed to be a universal phenomenon according to the one-pole model of Chapter 15. Again, modifications (i) to (iii) are needed to maintain the Regge pole interpretation.

Instead of trying to fit the data with only poles, however, it may be necessary to add moving cuts in J. This possibility has its origin in a theoretical question: what about exchange of two or more Regge trajectories? Is it already included in the Sommerfeld-Watson sum over one-pole exchanges, or does it give new terms? Note that the question did not arise in non-relativistic scattering; there, the Regge poles appeared in only one channel and were not exchanged. Accordingly, the question has been examined by explicit study of two-pole exchange diagrams, conducted by Amati, Fubini, and Stanghellini,[101] and more recently by Mandelstam.[102] The conclusion is that exchange of two or more poles may give new terms, which are moving cuts in J, although the matter is not fully settled.

For the benefit of interested theorists, we briefly discuss the details. The diagram studied by Amati, Fubini, and Stanghellini is shown in Fig. B-1. Mandelstam, however, found that the discontinuity across the cut cancels for this kind of diagram. He then proposed Fig. B-2 with multi-particle intermediate states as a diagram in which the discontinuity would not cancel. Since Mandelstam's diagram is more complicated, one might suspect that it also contains cancellations, which are harder to find than those of Fig. B-1. But Mandelstam has an independent argument for a cut in Fig. B-2. The argument involves the relativistic definition of the partial wave amplitude:

$$A_\ell(s) = \frac{1}{\pi} \int Q_\ell(z') \; A_z(z',s) \; dz' \qquad . \tag{13-4}$$

At $\ell = -1, -2, \ldots$, the function Q_ℓ becomes singular. In the z' integration, running from $z' = 1 + (m^2/q^2)$ to ∞, cancellations may occur so that A_ℓ is not generally singular at $\ell = -1, -2, \ldots$. But in the relativistic case there is a third double spectral function A_{tu}, which provides below threshold a separate piece of A_z running between finite limits in z. Gribov and Pomeranchuk[103)] showed that the integral over this piece does not cancel, and leads to essential singularities of A_ℓ at $\ell = -1, -2, \ldots$. A crisis arises if the total spin J includes intrinsic spins in addition to orbital angular momentum ℓ. The essential singularity at $\ell = -1$ may then propagate to physical spins $J = 0$ or 1, or even higher J where it violates the Froissart limit. Now, on account of its twisted structure, Fig. B-2 can be built up from spectral functions A_{tu}, whereas the simpler Fig. B-1 could not be. As a result, the Gribov-Pomeranchuk singularity must be faced in Fig. B-2, and Mandelstam argues that it disappears through a moving cut in J onto an unphysical sheet of the J plane. Figure B-1 has no Gribov-Pomeranchuk singularity, and therefore no "need" for a cut.

Leaving aside these difficult questions of cancellation, let us indicate how and where the cut arises in Fig. B-2. The total momentum transfer t is made up of two individual transfers t' and t", connected with exchange of spins $\alpha_1(t')$ and $\alpha_2(t'')$. The transfers t' and t" can add up to the total t in a whole continuum of ways, and correspondingly, a whole continuum of spins may be exchanged for a given t, instead of the discrete set of spins associated with Regge pole exchange.

Mathematically, the continuous set of spin exchanges is represented by a cut in J. From unitarity, one can show that the total spin exchanged is

$$J(t) = \alpha_1(t') + \alpha_2(t'') - 1 \quad , \tag{B-1}$$

and from this relation, together with constraints on physical momentum transfer (such as $t \leq 0$, $t' \leq 0$, $t'' \leq 0$ for equal mass particles), the location of the cut may be deduced. Several important conclusions of Regge pole theory remain unchanged:

i) From $\alpha(t) \leq 1$ at $t \leq 0$, we deduce $J(t) \leq 1$ at $t \leq 0$. Therefore, the Froissart bound is respected, the divergence problem is under control, and well-defined calculations involving all spins can be made.

ii) Regge pole theory had strengthened the Pomeranchuk conjecture, concerning the dominance of elastic over inelastic two-body reactions at high energy, by asserting that a charge-exchange or strangeness-exchange reaction was down by a power of s. We made predictions like

$$\frac{\frac{d\sigma}{dt}(\pi^- p \to \pi^- p)}{\frac{d\sigma}{dt}(\pi^- p \to \pi^0 n)} \sim s^{2(\alpha_{I=0} - \alpha_{I=1})} \tag{B-2}$$

where $\alpha_{I=0} > \alpha_{I=1}$. Now in forming $J(t)$ for charge (or S or B) exchange, at least one of the participating Regge poles must carry non-zero charge (or S or B), and we can deduce for example that

$$J_{I=1}(t = 0) \leq \alpha_{I=1}(t = 0) \quad . \tag{B-3}$$

Thus, exchange reactions are still down by powers of s.

iii) Bound states, resonances, and family relationships are still manifestations of Regge pole trajectories. (The possible effects of cuts in J at low energies are not understood.)

iv) The cuts appear as consequences of Regge poles and unitarity. Therefore, they do not violate maximal analyticity.

Some other aspects of the theory presented in Chapter 15 do change:

i) Exchange of two Pomeranchuk trajectories gives a maximum spin $J_{I=0}(t=0) = 1$, so the cut comes right up to the pole at $t = 0$. The cut and pole compete, with the pole eventually dominating by $\log s$ if the discontinuity R across the cut approaches a constant at its upper limit:

$$\int^{1} R(J)\, s^{J}\, dJ \underset{s \to \infty}{\sim} R(1) \int^{1} e^{J \ln s}\, dJ$$

$$\sim \frac{R(1)\, s}{\ln s} \quad . \qquad \text{(B-3)}$$

In any case, the approach to asymptotic behavior is slower when there are cuts. Note that while the high-energy limit of $\sigma^{tot}(pp)$ is approached logarithmically, a difference such as $\sigma^{tot}(pp) - \sigma^{tot}(p\bar{p})$ still vanishes like a power of s since both the Pomeranchuk pole and associated cut cancel in the difference.

ii) The cuts evidently complicate the phenomenological description by adding more parameters. An explicit theory of the cuts, involving calculation of cuts from multiple pole exchange, is needed to remove some of this uncertainty.

iii) At $t < 0$, the upper limit of the "Pomeranchuk cut" associated with two-pole exchange lies above the Pomeranchuk trajectory, the cut associated with three-pole exchange lies still higher, and the n-pole exchange cut approaches spin 1 at any t for sufficiently large n. To see why, recall that $t = (p_3 - p_1)^2$ is really momentum transfer squared. The momentum transfers obey triangle inequalities such as

$$\sqrt{|t|} \leq \sqrt{|t'|} + \sqrt{|t''|} \tag{B-4}$$

which permit t', t" as small as

$$|t'| = |t''| = \frac{|t|}{4} \quad , \tag{B-5}$$

for example. Using these permitted values and the approximation

$$\alpha(t) \simeq 1 + \alpha' t \tag{B-6}$$

for the Pomeranchuk trajectory, we find from (B-1)

$$J(t) = 1 + \alpha' \frac{t}{2} \quad , \tag{B-7}$$

which is a higher spin than $\alpha(t)$, especially at large $|t|$. As a consequence of the higher spin exchange, the differential cross section falls off more slowly with s, and the importance of the cut relative to the pole grows with increasing t.

If the residue of the pole is larger than the discontinuity of the cut, there may be an intermediate energy region where the pole dominates and the diffraction peak narrows with increasing energy, followed by a high-energy region where the cut takes over and the diffraction peak width tends to stabilize. In this model the cut would take over first at large $|t|$, then at progressively smaller $|t|$. Evidently, the model fits in with the new pp data[99] and smaller effective $d\alpha/dt$ mentioned at the beginning of this Addendum.

The possibility of cuts in J also affects the search for exchange of fixed J, or in other words, elementary particles. The elementary particle exchange gives terms $A \sim s^J$ which are easy to distinguish from Regge pole terms $A \sim s^{\alpha(t)}$, but harder to distinguish from "Regge cut" terms with their smaller slopes.

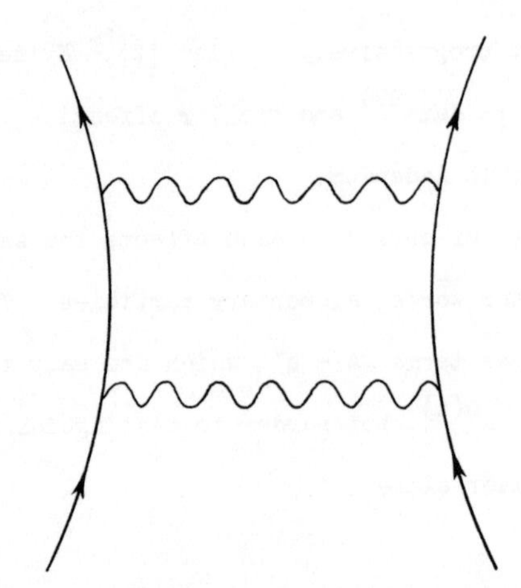

Figure B-1 The two-pole exchange diagram considered by Amati, Fubini, and Stanghellini. Wavy lines represent Regge poles, and straight lines represent ordinary particles.

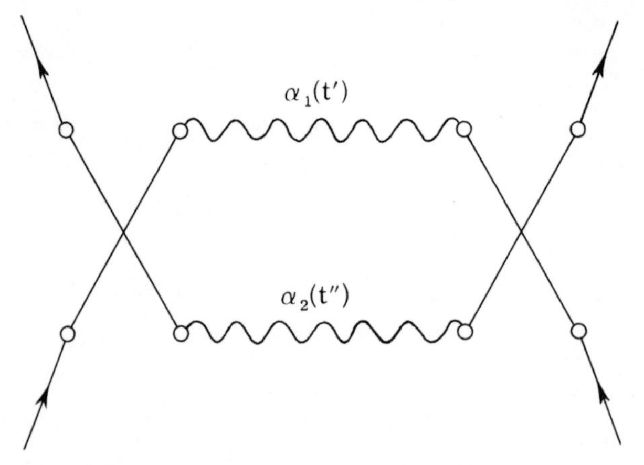

Figure B-2 The two-pole exchange diagram considered by Mandelstam.

REFERENCES

1. G. F. Chew and S. C. Frautschi, Phys. Rev. Letters 7, 394 (1961).
2. H. P. Stapp, Phys. Rev. 125, 2139 (1962); Lectures on S-Matrix Theory, W. A. Benjamin Inc., New York, 1963.
3. G. F. Chew and S. Mandelstam, Nuovo Cimento 19, 752 (1961); for a simple version, see F. Zachariasen, Phys. Rev. Letters 7, 112 (1961).
4. G. F. Chew and S. C. Frautschi, Phys. Rev. Letters 5, 580 (1960).
5. G. F. Chew and S. C. Frautschi, Phys. Rev. Letters 8, 41 (1962).
6. H. P. Noyes and D. Wong, Phys. Rev. Letters 3, 191 (1959).
7. G. F. Chew and S. Mandelstam, Phys. Rev. 119, 467 (1960).
8. J. Blatt and V. Weisskopf, Theoretical Nuclear Physics, Wiley, New York, p. 611 (1952).
9. G. Kallen and W. Pauli, Mat. Fys. Medd. Dan. Vid. Selsk. 30, No. 7 (1955).
10. W. Heisenberg, Nuclear Phys. 4, 532 (1957).
11. J. D. Bjorken and A.Goldberg, Nuovo Cimento 16, 539 (1960).
12. T. D. Lee, Phys. Rev. 95, 1329 (1954).
13. E. Wigner, Phys. Rev. 98, 145 (1955).
14. A. Martin, Supplement to Nuovo Cimento 21, 157 (1961).
15. L. Castillejo, R. H. Dalitz, and F. J. Dyson, Phys. Rev. 101, 453 (1956).
16. G. F. Chew, Lawrence Radiation Laboratory Report UCRL-9289 (1960).
17. N. Levinson, Mat. Fys. Medd. Dan. Vid. Selsk. 25, No. 9 (1949).
18. R. Omnes, Nuovo Cimento 21, 524 (1961).
19. R. Omnes, Nuovo Cimento 8, 316 (1958).
20. M. Froissart, Nuovo Cimento 22, 191 (1961).

21. S. Mandelstam, Phys. Rev. 112, 1344 (1958); 115, 1741, 1752 (1959).

22. R. Blankenbecler, M. L. Goldberger, N. N. Khuri, and S. B. Treiman, Ann. Phys. 10, 62 (1960).

23. T. Regge, Nuovo Cimento 14, 951 (1959).

24. T. Regge, Nuovo Cimento 18, 947 (1960).

25. A. Bottino, A. M. Longoni, and T. Regge, Nuovo Cimento 23, 954 (1962).

26. L. D. Landau, Nuclear Phys. 13, 181 (1959).

27. R. J. Eden, P. V. Landshoff, J. C. Polkinghorne, and J. C. Taylor, J. Math. Phys. 2, 656 (1961).

28. R. Karplus, C. Sommerfeld, and E. Wichmann, Phys. Rev. 111, 1187 (1958).

29. R. E. Cutkosky, Revs. Modern Phys. 33, 448 (1961).

30. S. Mandelstam, Phys. Rev. Letters 4, 84 (1960).

31. J. C. Polkinghorne, Phys. Rev. 128, 2898 (1962).

32. R. E. Cutkosky, J. Math. Phys. 1, 429 (1960); Phys. Rev. Letters 4, 624 (1960).

33. G. F. Chew and S. C. Frautschi, Phys. Rev. 124, 264 (1961).

34. J. Charap and S. Fubini, Nuovo Cimento 14, 540 (1959).

35. G. F. Chew, Phys. Rev. 112, 1380 (1958).

36. For a review, see M. Moravscik and H. P. Noyes, Ann. Rev. Nuclear Sci. 11 (1961).

37. E. Ferrari and F. Selleri, Phys. Rev. Letters 7, 387 (1961).

38. G. F. Chew, S. Mandelstam, and H. P. Noyes, Phys. Rev. 119, 478 (1960).

39. W. Frazer and J. Fulco, Phys. Rev. Letters 2, 365 (1959); Phys. Rev. 117, 1609 (1960).

40. M. L. Goldberger, M. T. Grisaru, S. W. McDowell, and D. Wong, Phys. Rev. 120, 2250 (1960).

41. A. C. Hearn, Nuovo Cimento 21, 333 (1961).

42. G. F. Chew and F. E. Low, Phys. Rev. 101, 1570 (1956).

43. W. Frazer and J. Fulco, Phys. Rev. 119, 1420 (1960).

44. S. Frautschi and D. Walecka, Phys. Rev. 120, 1486 (1960).

45. J. Bowcock, W. Cottingham, and D. Lurié, Phys. Rev. Letters 5, 386 (1960).

46. G. F. Chew and S. C. Frautschi, Phys. Rev. 123, 1478 (1961); K. Wilson, unpublished Harvard University Physics Department preprint (1960); K. A. Ter-Martirosyan, Soviet Phys. JETP 12, 575 (1961).

47. H. Lehmann, Nuovo Cimento 10, 579 (1958).

48. M. Froissart, Phys. Rev. 123, 1053 (1961).

49. M. Gell-Mann and M. L. Goldberger, Phys. Rev. Letters 9, 275 (1962).

50. H. Poincaré, Rendiconti Circolo Mat. Palermo 29, 169 (1910); J. W. Nicholson, Phil. Mag. 19, 516 (1910); 20, 157 (1910); Messenger Math. 37, 84 (1907).

51. G. N. Watson, Proc. Roy. Soc. (London) 95, 83 (1918).

52. A. Sommerfeld, Partial Differential Equations in Physics, Academic Press Inc., New York, p. 282 (1949).

53. A. O. Barut and F. Calogero, Phys. Rev. 128, 1383 (1962).

54. M. Froissart, J. Math. Phys. 3, 922 (1962).

55. S. Mandelstam, Ann. Phys. 19, 254 (1962).

56. R. G. Newton, J. Math. Phys. 3, 867 (1962).

57. E. J. Squires, Nuovo Cimento 25, 242 (1962).

58. G. Prosperi, Nuovo Cimento 24, 957 (1962).

59. H. Cheng and R. Nunez-Lagos, Nuovo Cimento 26, 177 (1962).

60. See, for example, Morse and Feshbach, Methods of Theoretical Physics, McGraw-Hill Inc., New York, Part I, p. 593 (1953).

61. A. O. Barut and D. E. Zwanziger, Phys. Rev. 127, 974 (1962).

62. A. Ahmadzadeh, P. G. Burke, and C. Tate, Lawrence Radiation Laboratory Report UCRL-10216 (1962); C. Lovelace and D. Masson, Proceedings of the 1962 International Conference on High-Energy Physics at CERN, p. 510.

63. M. Gell-Mann, Proceedings of the 1962 International Conference on High Energy Physics at CERN, p. 539.

64. V. Singh, Phys. Rev. 127, 632 (1962).

65. V. N. Gribov and I. Ya. Pomeranchuk, Phys. Rev. Letters 9, 238 (1962).

66. N. Limić, Nuovo Cimento 26, 581 (1962).

67. E. Predazzi and T. Regge, Nuovo Cimento 24, 518 (1962).

68. G. F. Chew, S. C. Frautschi, and S. Mandelstam, Phys. Rev. 126, 1202 (1962).

69. V. N. Gribov, J. Exptl. Theor. Phys. (USSR) 41, 667, 1962 (1961), translation: Soviet Physics JETP 14, 478, 1395 (1962).

70. R. Blankenbecler and M. L. Goldberger, Phys. Rev. 126, 766 (1962).

71. C. Lovelace, Nuovo Cimento 25, 730 (1962).

72. G. F. Chew and S. C. Frautschi, Phys. Rev. Letters 7, 394 (1961).

73. G. F. Chew, Revs. Modern Phys. 34, 394 (1962).

74. S. C. Frautschi, M. Gell-Mann, and F. Zachariasen, Phys. Rev. 126, 2204 (1962).

75. B. M. Udgaonkar, Phys. Rev. Letters 8, 142 (1962).

76. V. N. Gribov and I. Ya. Pomeranchuk, Phys. Rev. Letters 8, 343 (1962).

77. V. N. Gribov and I. Ya. Pomeranchuk, Phys. Rev. Letters 8, 412 (1962).

78. G. Domokos, Proceedings of the 1962 International Conference on High Energy Physics at CERN, p. 553.

79. A. Martin, Physics Letters 1, 72 (1962).

80. R. Omnes, Nuovo Cimento 25, 806 (1962).

81. K. Bardakci, Phys. Rev. 127, 1832 (1962).

82. B. Lee and R. Sawyer, Phys. Rev. 127, 2266 (1962).

83. D. Amati, S. Fubini, and A. Stanghellini, Physics Letters 1, 29 (1962).

84. See, for example, the talks by Perkins, Cocconi, Winter, and Morrison, Proceedings of the International Conference on Theoretical Aspects of Very High-Energy Phenomena, CERN (1961).

85. I. Ya. Pomeranchuk, Soviet Physics JETP 3, 306 (1956); I. Ya. Pomeranchuk and L. B. Okun, Soviet Physics JETP 3, 307 (1956).

86. I. Ya. Pomeranchuk, Soviet Physics JETP 7, 499 (1958).

87. G. Cocconi, A. N. Diddens, E. Lillithun, G. Manning, A. E. Taylor, T. G. Walker, and A. M. Wetherell, Phys. Rev. Letters 7, 450 (1961); G. Cocconi, Proceedings of the 1962 International Conference on High Energy Physics at CERN, p. 883.

88. K. Igi, Phys. Rev. Letters 9, 76 (1962).

89. M. Gell-Mann, Phys. Rev. Letters 8, 263 (1962).

90. Selove, Hagopian, Brody, Baker, and Leboy, Phys. Rev. Letters 9, 272 (1962).

91. Veillet, Hennessey, Bingham, Block, Drijard, Lagarrique, Mittner, Rousset, Bellini, di Corato, Fiorini, and Negri, Phys. Rev. Letters 10, 29 (1963).

92. A. H. Rosenfeld, Proceedings of the 1962 International Conference on High Energy Physics at CERN, p. 326.

93. R. Capps, Phys. Rev. Letters 10, 312 (1963).

94. R. Cutkosky, Phys. Rev. 131, 1888 (1963).

95. E. Abers, F. Zachariasen, and C. Zemach, (to be published in Phys. Rev., 1963).

96. R. Blankenbecler, L. F. Cook, and M. L. Goldberger, Phys. Rev. Letters 8, 463 (1962).

97. N. N. Khuri, Phys. Rev. 130, 429 (1963).

98. E. Jones, Lawrence Radiation Laboratory Report UCRL-10700 (1963).

99. Foley, Lindenbaum, Love, Ozaki, Russell, and Yuan, Phys. Rev. Letters 10, 376 (1963).

100. Foley, Lindenbaum, Love, Ozaki, Russell, and Yuan, Phys. Rev. Letters 10, 543 (1963).

101. D. Amati, S. Fubini, and A. Stanghellini, Physics Letters 1, 29 (1962).

102. S. Mandelstam, preprints (1963).

103. V. N. Gribov and I. Ya. Pomeranchuk, Proceedings of the 1962 International Conference on High-Energy Physics at CERN, p. 522.

INDEX